GARRATT LOCOMOTIVES OF THE WORLD

GARRATT LOCOMOTIVES OF THE WORLD

A.E. DURRANT

DAVID & CHARLES
Newton Abbot   London   North Pomfret (Vt)

British Library Cataloguing in Publication Data

Durrant, A. E.
 The Garratt locomotive.
 1. Garratt steam locomotives
 I. Title
 625.5'61   TJ625.G2/

 ISBN 0-7153-7641-1

First published in 1969 as *The Garratt Locomotive*
This completely revised and enlarged edition published in 1981

Printed in Great Britain
by Ebenezer Baylis & Son Ltd., Worcester
for David & Charles (Publishers) Limited
Brunel House   Newton Abbot   Devon

Published in the United States of America
by David & Charles Inc
North Pomfret   Vermont 05053 USA

Jacket photographs
*(front) In the 1960s and 1970s, train after train left
Pietermaritzburg behind double-headed Garratts.
Mason's Mill shed allocation was 101 Garratts,
including 74 massive GMAMs. Rounding the horseshoe curve at City View, a pair of GMAMs attack
the first of several 1 in 30 gradients on the line to
Greytown.*   A. E. Durrant

*(back) Sunset on Garratts. The Garratt has
disappeared in many parts of the world, although
being given a new lease of life in Zimbabwe. This
sunset silhouette of an ex-RR 16th class at Landau 3
colliery, clearly outlines the type's salient features —
two engine units with boiler unit slung between.*
A. E. Durrant

Frontispiece
(above) Ingane indlovu, ubaba indlovu, *and* umama
indlovu — *baby, father, and mother elephants in the
shape of 14A, 20A and 15A Garratts line up in
Bulawayo running shed.*   A. E. Durrant

(below) Indlovu *(elephant), a typical nameplate with
flanking three-rail symbol, as being applied to
Garratts of the National Railways of Zimbabwe.*
A. E. Durrant

Contents

Introduction

The year 1968, when the manuscript for the original edition of *The Garratt Locomotive* was completed, marked the end of a fifty-nine year era, during which the Garratt type of locomotive was produced. Starting with a small two-foot-gauge machine for Tasmania, Beyer Peacock & Co Ltd of Gorton, Manchester, developed the type for all kinds of services, from shunting to express passenger work, and the Garratt was exported to every continent. By 1968 the wheel had turned full circle and what are possibly the last Garratts to be built were being completed in South Africa. These were for the two-foot-gauge, a curious coincidence.

While Beyer Peacock's name has always been associated with the Garratt type, which this company called a 'Beyer Garratt', it will probably be a surprise to many to learn that only about two-thirds of all Garratts were built in Manchester, some being built by other British firms, and many abroad. Of this other third, many were built under licence from Beyer Peacock, while others were clearly 'pirated'.

Much has been written about Garratts, most of the Beyer Peacock designs being fully described in the railway and technical press, so that it is not the intention of this book simply to repeat such information. Indeed, the constructional details have been commented on but briefly and in the tables of principal dimensions which are appended to each chapter, a literature reference has been given which will enable the researcher to consult the appropriate books or magazines for further information.

This book traces the development of the Garratt as a locomotive type, and, in the first chapter, reviews the principal alternative types of articulated steam locomotives which preceded or offered competition to the Garratt. Details of work performed by the various Garratt classes have been included wherever available, this information comprising the routes worked, the loads hauled on the ruling gradients, and any other relevant information of a similar nature. Complete lists of all Garratts built have been included, together with the builders' numbers and dates, details of locomotives sold to other railways or industrial concerns etc, and scrapping dates. This information has been updated from the original volume.

Every possible user and builder of Garratts was contacted by the author in an effort to obtain up-to-date and authentic information, although in certain cases the railway no longer exists or the builder has gone out of business, as have Beyer Peacock themselves. Of the remainder, many replied, some did not, particularly and predictably including most of the South American railways, while of the manufacturers, one firm of over a century's standing, has been so brainwashed by the glamour of its new diesels and electrics as to deny not only that it had built Garratts but that it had built any steam locomotives whatever! Even a photostat of its prewar advertisement failed to produce any positive response!

Some mention has been made of various personalities relevant to the Garratt story, although this aspect has not been dwelt upon. Apart from H. W. Garratt himself, W. Cyril Williams, who was employed upon the South African Railways, probably had the greatest influence in promoting the Garratt. Connected with the trials of the initial SAR engine, he became enthused with the concept and joined Beyer Peacock as technical sales representative, subsequently travelling the world selling Garratts, and presenting a number of papers, to which reference is made in the Bibliography.

In the twelve years which have elapsed since the publication of the first edition of *The Garratt Locomotive* developments have mainly been negative, with Garratts disappearing completely from regular service in Europe, Asia, Australia and South America, today being found only in Africa, as forecast in that book. Although based on the earlier work this present volume is much more than just a new edition and warrants a new title. The text has been completely revised and totally re-written where necessary, to incorporate further information, and to update the position as far as is known, to the end of 1980.

Even in Africa, the Garratt has become a severely endangered species, having ceased operation in East Africa and the various West African states which were once users. Giant South African Railways has only a third of its former Garratt roster in stock, many of those remaining being out of use, while in Angola, Mozambique, and Zambia, the decline of these country's economies has been equalled by their railway systems, whose installations, including Garratts, have been neglected to the point of dereliction.

Fortunately, all is not gloom. In South Africa, while SAR responds to the oil crisis by ordering more diesels, industrial users have taken up the government's call to save oil by buying up steam locomotives from SAR, several of which are Garratts, in a general move to reverse previous dieselisation policies. The most heartening situation exists in Zimbabwe, where the former dieselisation policy has been totally reversed to include both electrification plus the very extensive rehabilitation of nearly a hundred Garratts for further use into the 1990s.

Furthermore, the ever escalating oil crisis has prompted several investigations and studies into the viability of modern coal-burning steam power; whereas in 1968 it could comfortably be written that the last Garratts had just been built, 1980 sees the position where sophisticated Garratts, with compound expansion, condensors, and advanced combustion cycles, are on more than one drawing board. It is impossible, of course, to predict the future in these turbulent times, where the oil crisis has been misrepresented as an 'energy crisis' (although no other forms of energy are endangered), but it is fairly safe to assume that the old Garratt rhythm, the stuttering, unsynchronised, exhaust from independent engine units, will be stilled by the year 2000. Modern Garratts, if built, will have exhaust beats softened by compounding and evened to a dreary whine by condensing gear.

The whole story, past, present, and possible future is produced within a book with more and larger pages than before, in order to encompass the greater amount of information and variety of illustration showing these magnificent locomotives hard at work. A colour section is an innovation, and will be appreciated particularly by the growing numbers of photographers who work in this medium.

A. E. Durrant Springs,
South Africa

Chapter 1

Articulated Locomotives

Compared with road traffic, the railway, as has frequently been written, possesses the great advantage not only of having a low rolling resistance, due to the running of one hard, smooth surface over another, but also that the vehicles are self steering by the action and reaction of wheel flanges upon the rails. However, this results in an anomaly: although a vehicle mounted on two or more parallel axles, and running on parallel rails, is perfect upon straight track, once it enters a curve the geometry becomes incorrect, and the wheel is not facing the same direction as the track, but lies at an angle to it. With a short wheelbase vehicle and a large radius curve, this angle is small, and its effect negligible, but as railways developed and penetrated terrain more difficult than that of the earliest lines, it became increasingly necessary to run longer vehicles around sharper curves than hitherto.

As far as wagons and carriages were concerned, the problem was relatively small. One could either use a large number of short vehicles or alternatively mount a longer one on bogies. The same solutions, of course, were available to locomotive engineers, but here, technology and economics posed limitations not met with in the rolling stock. To start with, the use of short-wheelbase locomotives in multiple was uneconomical both in first cost and also in operation, particularly as each unit needed its own crew. The double-bogie locomotive was rather beyond the capabilities of early engineers as, even with the low-pressure unsuperheated steam then in use, the development of successful flexible steam pipe joints was outside their capacity. This was in no way a reflection upon the ingenuity of the early designers of articulated locomotives, ie, those mounted on two or more power-driven bogies, but simply reflected the fact that the materials obtainable both for manufacture and for lubrication, and the machine tools available, were simply not up to the demands of the locomotive engineer. In fact, the earliest designs of flexible steam pipe joints differed little in principle from those used today, it being technique rather than fundamental thinking which has improved.

Given these difficulties, together with the failure of the earliest articulated designs, it was hardly surprising that engineers experimented, albeit cautiously, with the coupling together of more and more driving wheels. Four and six-wheels coupled were soon in regular use and, during the 1860s, eight-coupled engines became relatively common in the USA and on the continent of Europe. Confidence, possibly over-confidence, in these, led to a small rash of ten-coupled designs soon after, but this type did not come into general use until the turn of the century, since when it spread widely, again mainly on the continent of Europe and USA. The ten-coupled locomotive has remained the generally accepted maximum for rigid framed locomotives although a number of twelve-coupled types have been constructed and have given little or no trouble in running. The type was recently in use in Austria, Bulgaria, Jugoslavia, and Java, these all being small-wheeled engines with the total rigid wheelbase but little or no longer than many ten-coupled types with larger wheels. An exception was the Union Pacific 4—12—2 with 5ft 7in wheels and a 30ft 8in coupled wheelbase which nevertheless was a very successful machine of which no fewer than 88 were built over a period of years, and whose life as a class extended to 29 years, from 1926 to 1955, and would doubtless have extended further but for the plague of diesels which invaded the United States railroads from the end of the war. The only fourteen-coupled locomotive built, the Russian class AA 4—14—4, was with its 5ft 3in wheels and 33ft 0in coupled wheelbase, not such a vastly longer machine than the UP type but sufficiently so to make it ruinous on the existing Russian track and useless as a traffic machine. The increase was too great in one step; had Lomonossov's proposed compound 0—12—0 been built first, then possibly sufficient experience might have been gained to make a shorter and smaller wheeled 4—14—4 a success. As it was, during the last war, when the logistics of supplying the Russian front were straining Hitler's transport system to the utmost, a 2—14—0 designed by the firm of Schichau, of Elbing, was one of a number of proposals for a powerful but light axle load locomotive for the Russian front. This, with 4ft 3in wheels and 30ft 7in wheelbase, had every chance of success, being designed for a curve of 140m (460ft, approx 7 chains) and backed by Germany's experience with the forty-four members comprising the former Württemburg State railway's 'K' class 2—12—0; the collapse of the invasion, however, led to the design being stillborn, so we never shall know how it would have performed.

Whilst this development of the rigid-framed locomotive was approaching its maximum, various types of articulated machines were also developing. These were ahead of the rigid types because of doubts as to the ability of the latter to traverse curves safely and efficiently, and in early days, before the general adoption of spring-controlled sideplay for axles within a rigid frame, these doubts were probably well founded. There was, however, one design which surprisingly, was not widely adopted, although it was probably ahead of contemporary technology. This was Petiet's 0—6—6—0T of 1862—3 which had twelve driving wheels, coupled in two groups of six, within a rigid frame. The second and fifth axles, being the main drivers, were rigid, the others being connected by Beugniot levers to control the lateral displacement on curves. The twenty locomotives built for the Northern Railway of France were the most powerful locomotives in the world at the time, and while they led to the export of another couple to the Zaragoza—Alsasua Railway, in Spain, the conception of a 'duplex' engine on a rigid frame lay dormant for seventy-five years when it was taken up again in the USA by the Baltimore & Ohio and Pennsylvania Railroads.

Meanwhile, early articulated locomotives had appeared, and in general, where eight driving wheels were required, two four-wheel bogies were utilized. As a general rule, apart from small engines for severely curved branches and light railways, the minimum size for an articulated locomotive grew with the development of successful rigid-framed locomotives. For example, as rigid eight-coupled engines became a normal thing, articulateds were not used until traffic outgrew the eight-coupled, whereupon six-coupled articulateds came into use until generally superseded by ten-coupled power with heavier axle loads. This generally represented the limit for rigid engines, and thereafter, the articulated with eight, or exceptionally, ten-coupled units held undisputed sway. There were also many railways, particularly in colonial and similar areas, where the ten-coupled type was never popular, and six-coupled articulateds were used in their place.

Having discussed briefly the place of the articulated locomotive, and its *raison d'être*, we can now consider the principal types, their origins, advantages, and limitations. There have, in the history of the steam locomotive, been a vast variety of articulateds, most of which were unsuccessful, and these have been catalogued exhaustively in Lionel Wiener's classic book *Articulated Locomotives*, published in 1930. Here, we are only concerned with those which achieved some measures of success as it is these which led to, and to a certain extent competed with, the Garratt type, which forms the subject of this book. It is interesting to note, incidentally, that these early types were not necessarily known by the name of the originator, but by that of who-ever largely developed and exploited the principle.

What appears to be indisputably the earliest articulated was that designed by Horatio Allen, for the Charleston & South Carolina Railway, USA, and built by the West Point foundry in 1832. This was the embryonic origin of what became known as the Fairlie type, of which Allen's engine contained all the basic ingredients. It had a central firebox with boiler barrels extending each way to a smokebox, with chimneys at each extremity, a curious feature being that each end comprised twin barrels making four in all! As if to compensate for this extravagant use of barrels, the bogies, which were of the 2—2—0 type, had but a single central cylinder apiece and were mounted on wooden frames. The idea was to obtain a low centre of gravity, then thought necessary, and the arrangement allowed each crank to rotate between the twin barrels, which were scarcely above the driving axle. Illustrations now available of this locomotive seem somewhat unconvincing, and it would appear that the driver stood on top of the firebox, next to the off-centre dome. Exactly where the fireman stood, or how he fired it (the sides of the firebox being largely obscured by the wheels), are a mystery, as are details of where the fuel and water supply were carried.

However, it was a start, and led to the second engine of the type, almost two decades later, when designs and trial locomotives were called for the famous Semmering contest in Austria, during 1851. Of the four contestants, two were full articulateds, and that submitted by John Cockerill et Cie of Seraing, Belgium, was the next stage in the Fairlie type. This was an 0—4—4—0T and each engine unit had outside frames with inside cylinders. The boiler had a single outer firebox containing two inner fireboxes, each of which discharged gases through an oval boiler barrel to its own smokebox and chimney. Each barrel had its own dome, from which was fed the steam to the cylinders at that end. Apart from the oval barrels, the design appears well worked out and it is rather surprising that the locomotive was a failure, and beaten by the extremely curious contraptions that actually won the contest, but were not repeated in service.

An offshoot of this type now claims our attention, this being the back-to-back twin locomotive which first appeared on the Giovi incline in Italy in 1856 and reappeared spasmodically until the last examples were built for the German

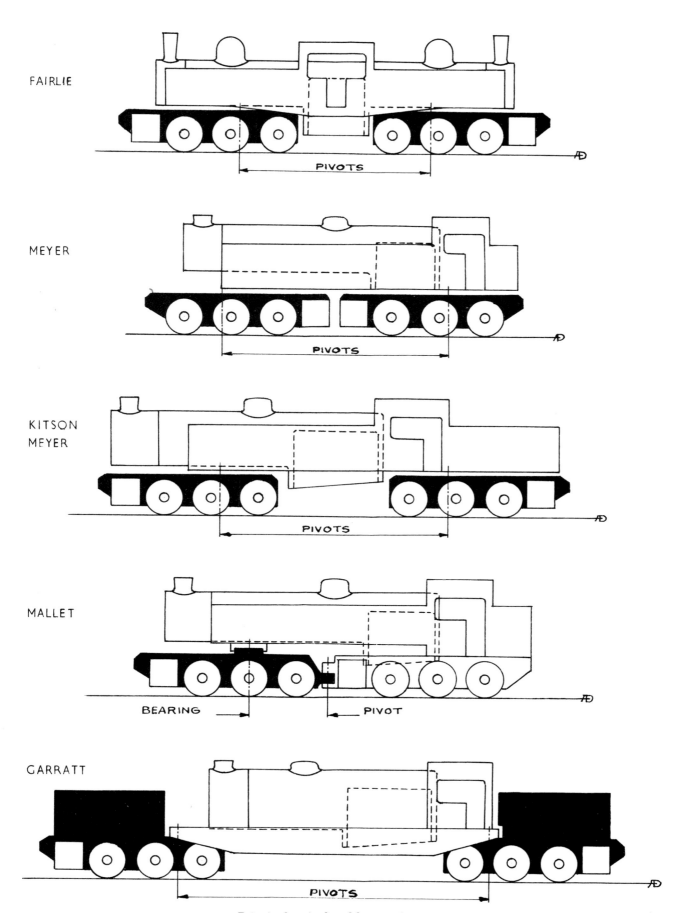

FAIRLIE

MEYER

KITSON MEYER

MALLET

GARRATT

PIVOTS

PIVOTS

PIVOTS

BEARING   PIVOT

PIVOTS

Principal articulated locomotive types.

The largest Fairlies built were these 102 ton examples for the Mexicano Railway, incorporated much later into the Mexican National system. Despite their impressive proportions, these engines were devoid of superheaters or modern valve arrangements and were soon replaced by electrification. English Electric

Military Railways during the first world war. These were simply two small tank engines, without rear bunkers, which were coupled together, cab to cab like Siamese Twins. These had the advantage of giving double locomotive power, as in a true articulated, yet retaining but one engine crew, whilst they also dispensed with the need for flexible steampipe joints, so long a bugbear on articulateds. Nevertheless, the difficulty of controlling the units effectively, plus their undoubtedly rough riding, made the type generally unpopular and rarely used.

Robert Fairlie, a Scotsman, took out his patent for a double-ended articulated locomotive in May 1863, and this was for a machine substantially as Cockerill's Semmering locomotive, except that whereas the 'Seraing' had the buffing and drawgear mounted on the main superstructure, Fairlie mounted his on the power bogies, this difference probably being sufficient to secure the patent. Whereas Cockerill produced their design for a specific contest, and, disheartened by failure, never revived it, Fairlie was a keen pro-

tagonist of his version, and expended such energy in its promotion that it became the established form of articulated steam locomotive for many years, the last examples being built during the first world war. The great bulk of Fairlies built were total adhesion 0—4—4—0T or 0—6—6—0T, although a few 2—4—4—2T and 2—6—6—2T were also constructed. Compared with certain other articulateds the Fairlie had the advantage of a firebox unrestricted by frames or wheels beneath it, thus allowing for good air intake and ashpan conditions. However, the poor fireman, positioned side-saddle as it were, had little room to swing his shovel even on a small Fairlie, and the more the boiler tended to fill the loading gauge, the more cramped his quarters became, providing a human limit to the size of the locomotive. A mechanical stoker would be difficult to apply, due to the right-angled bend involved, and it is significant that the largest Fairlies built were for Mexico, and oil fired. Further limitations were in the amount of fuel and water which could be carried, these having to be above and beside the

boiler so that again, as the engine and boiler grew in size, more water and fuel were needed, but there was less room in which to put them! A separate water tender could have been coupled up, thus easing the situation, but before the Fairlie reached this stage it was superseded by alternative types of articulated locomotives. The Fairlie never received such modern devices as poppet, or even piston valves, or superheaters. All had straightforward two-cylinder simple expansion power bogies. The last built, in 1915, were the so-called Pechôt-Bourdon Locos, for the French Military 60cm-gauge trench railways. The last survivors in service are on the Festiniog Railway in North Wales, whilst a few others are preserved here and there—about half a dozen in all. It is interesting to note that the Festiniog Fairlies are now oil-fired, but that was more to save servicing costs.

The next type to be considered is the Meyer, and it is first necessary to define what can be termed the basic Meyer type, as Wiener differentiates between the Meyer and the du Bousquet on buffing and drawbar positions only, without any other basic feature being different. Thus, the present writer would define a Meyer as being an articulated locomotive having two individual rod-driven power bogies, upon which is pivoted a single superstructure carrying the boiler, cab, fuel, and water. Given these terms of reference, which the writer contends are correct, then the first Meyer type locomotive was also one of the Semmering contestants, the 'Wiener Neustadt' built at that town by the firm of the same name. As in most early Meyers, the cylinders were grouped at the inner ends of the bogies, thereby enabling the main steam pipes from the dome to be relatively short and direct. Apart from the twin power bogies, the Meyer generally had the appearance of a normal tank engine and the Wiener Neustadt was no exception. Wiener classes this as a du Bousquet, having buffing and drawgear on the main frame, and Jean-Jacques Meyer of Mulhouse in France patented his version with buffing and drawgear in the bogies in March 1861.

The du Bousquet articulated locomotives were basically of the Meyer configuration. SNCF No 031.130.TA.19 poses in Paris Bobigny depot in October 1950. A. E. Durrant

The Meyer was the principal competitor to the Fairlie, and was largely built during the same period. Compared with the Fairlie, it was at a disadvantage in having wheels, axles, brake gear, etc under the firebox, which thus limited the firebox depth and the ashpan capacity. On the other hand, the fireman occupied his normal position behind the back plate, and there was ample room for him to fire, and also adequate space for a normal bunker behind him. Thus the general restrictions of a Meyer were little more than in an ordinary tank engine, and the type had the advantage of improved flexibility for a given number of driving wheels. There was little to choose between the riding characteristics of a Meyer or a Fairlie, and both largely remained special purpose engines.

The Meyer was quite often compounded, with the low-pressure cylinders naturally on the leading unit, and probably the best and certainly the largest examples of these were the 0—6—2 + 2—6—0T designed by du Bousquet and built for the Northern Railway of France in 1905—11, the Andalucian of Spain, and for China. Of these, the French type were the last survivors, lasting until 1950—51. The Saxon State Railways were great believers in Meyers, and built numerous compound examples for both standard and 750mm gauges until 1921, many of the narrow-gauge examples still being in use in East Germany. No doubt these would normally have been the last built, but Messrs W. G. Bagnall revived the type for plantation work, and built them in the nineteen-fifties, mainly for South Africa. These little engines are superheated and have piston valves and have doubtless been favoured due to their very compact build, compared with a Garratt of comparable size and power.

The principal disadvantage of the Meyer, that of restricted firebox and ashpan, was eliminated by Messrs Kitson of Leeds, by the simple expedient of spreading the bogies further apart, and allowing the firebox to drop between. This they termed a Kitson-Meyer, but here again they had been forestalled, by the Baldwin works of Philadelphia, USA, who had built a similar machine in 1892, an eight-cylinder Vauclain compound for the Sinnemahoning Valley RR.

The earlier Kitson-Meyers, including the Baldwin, had the cylinders curiously placed at the rear ends of each bogie, and on a number of these, the exhaust of the rear cylinders went out via a separate chimney which passed through the rear tank, thus slightly pre-heating the feed water. This had the disadvantage of relying only on the exhaust of the forward unit to induce the boiler draught, which probably caused steaming

The Kitson-Meyer improved on the original Meyer by spreading the bogies apart, giving room for the firebox to drop between, anticipating the Garratt in this respect. 0—6—6—0T No 59, on the Taltal Railway, Chile, was the last working example of the breed, and is seen here at work in 1977. Note the curious double exhaust, the rear pair of cylinders exhausting through a separate chimney behind the cab.
A. E. Durrant

The so-called 'Modified Fairlie', a variation on the Kitson-Meyer theme introduced by North British to combat the Beyer Garratt. North British Locomotive Co

troubles. After passing through one or two curious phases such as having a tender at the firebox end, alternatively a tender at the smokebox end plus 2—6—0 + 2—6—0 wheel arrangement (counting from the cab end), and finally a 2—6—6—4 with a semi-articulated tender, on the firebox end, the Kitson-Meyer eventually settled down to a sensible arrangement with cylinders at the outer ends of each bogie, but both exhausting through the smokebox. By this stage, which is what it should always have been, it was a very good articulated engine, but by then the Garratt, which was even better, was well in its stride and the Kitson-Meyer, with Kitson themselves, finally died out. But for the advent of the Garratt, it would undoubtedly have had a better innings than was actually the case, with less than fifty years from the Baldwin originals to the very fine 1935 2—8—8—2T built for the Colombian National Railways.

Two types of locomotive have been built which are basically Kitson-Meyers but have never previously been referred to as such. First are the so-called 'Modified Fairlie' locomotives, built by the North British Locomotive Co and later by Henschel for the South African Railways. These were quite clearly desperate attempts to get on the Garratt bandwagon which was just becoming an obvious success and which was no doubt adequately covered by patents of Messrs Beyer Peacock. Its closest competitor was the Kitson-Meyer, also doubtless covered by Kitson patents, and North British, not wishing to be left out of a potentially large market, produced this effort. The 'Modified Fairlie' had no more in common with the Fairlie proper than the fact that it was a double-bogie steam locomotive. In all basic ingredients it was a Kitson-Meyer, but with the superstructure frame extended so that the side tanks were placed ahead of the smokebox, thus making it look like a Garratt!

A gullible customer was found in the shape of Col Collins, chief mechanical engineer of the South African Railways, who was a rather over-enthusiastic devotee of articulateds and willing to buy anything that was driven by steam and could bend in the middle. Starting with the proto-type 2—6—2 + 2—6—2 class FC in 1925, this was barely in service before four larger locos class FD were ordered, and again these were just about put to work when Henschels won an order for eleven 2—8—2 + 2—8—2 examples, classed HF.

The deficiencies of the 'Modified Fairlie' were such that the bigger the engine the worse they became. With both front and rear tanks canti-levered out, the water sloshing about put heavy

16

stress on the pivots which, predictably, then became troublesome and expensive to maintain. To give Collins his due, he was probably endeavouring to avoid placing all his eggs in Beyer Peacock's basket, and the SAR by then had tried everything else. A couple of straight Fairlies, to which classes FA and FB were presumably posthumously allocated, were long since defunct, and one of the queerer and earlier forms of Kitson-Meyer had been tried and found wanting. A fleet of small-wheeled Mallets was in use, but whilst these pulled well, they were sluggish at speed. One was even a superheated simple, the first of its type in the world, whilst another, never repeated anywhere, had larger driving wheels on the low-pressure unit than the high. So poor Collins experimented with the 'Modified Fairlie', the only person to do so, when he would have been better off with the modern form of Kitson-Meyer. The 'Modified Fairlie' did not last long, and as soon as new Garratts were available after the war, were replaced, the FC having already disappeared in 1939.

The final type of locomotive which, strictly speaking, is of the Kitson-Meyer type, was Bulleid's controversial 'Leader' class of the Southern Railway. Whether or not these would ever have been made to operate successfully, with

the designer's 'push' behind them, will always remain a railway enigma, but having examined both the locomotives and their drawings it is the author's opinion that they would not.

Having dealt with the other principal articulated types, we now come to the Mallet which, if sheer numbers is anything to go by, counts as the most successful articulated type built, although strictly speaking, it is only semi-articulated.

Anatole Mallet, a Swiss, invented the system, and it came about largely as a sideline of his experience in compounding, carried out with small 0—4—2T and 0—6—0T engines on the Bayonne and Biarritz railway in south-west France. When he came to apply his compounding methods to narrow-gauge articulated locomotives, he was rightly rather apprehensive of the possible success or otherwise of the flexible steampipe connections to the high-pressure bogie and after various deliberations he took out in 1884 the French patent which bears his name. The Mallet principle consists of having the boiler mounted on the mainframe of the locomotive in the normal way, with the steam supply led directly to the cylinders on that frame, this being the high-pressure unit. Jointed to the front of this frame is another, with a further set of cylinders, this forming the low-pressure unit. This front

17

The classic compound Mallet is represented here by PNKA 2—8—8—0 No DD5208, heading a passenger train at Tjitjalenka, Java, in 1971. Note the huge low pressure cylinders on the leading engine unit.
A. E. Durrant

frame is not a bogie, as in other articulated types, but a form of radial or pony truck, pivoted outside and behind its wheelbase (between the high-pressure cylinders) and with the load from the superstructure carried through a sliding bearing which, whilst not a pivot point, carries control springs for sideways movement. The great advantage was that the high-pressure steampipes were rigidly mounted, and only the low-pressure pipes had to have flexible joints.

The first Mallet, built in 1887, was a small 0—4—4—0T for a narrow-gauge line, and the type soon proved immensely popular, and eventually hundreds were built to various gauges and for numerous railways throughout Europe and elsewhere. Larger types such as 2—4—4—0T, 0—4—4—2T and 0—6—6—0T were also built, plus other rarer types including even locos with asymmetrical numbers of coupled wheels such as the 2—4—6—0T which just survives in Portugal. The biggest Mallet tanks were the twenty-five 0—8—8—0T built for Bavaria in 1914 and 1923, for banking duties.

Unlike most other articulated types, the Mallet was found to be as suitable for tender as for tank engines, and in 1893 the first 0—4—4—0s with separate tenders were built for the Prussian and Baden State railways. A few other Mallet tender engines were supplied here and there, but only two European countries possessed them in quantity, Hungary which developed them up to the 2—6—6—0 type in 1914 and Jugoslavia which inherited many of the Hungarian locomotives and also had fifty 760mm gauge 2—6—6—0s supplied.

Meanwhile, in the USA the Baltimore and Ohio RR, faced with an operating bottleneck in its coal-hauling route through the Alleghenies, perceived that these little European locomotives had in them the features which they could use. Hence, in 1904 there was placed in service No 2400, a huge 0—6—6—0 Mallet tender loco, which promptly, and briefly, captured the title of the 'world's largest locomotive'. Such was the success of this Alco giant that orders were soon pouring in from all over the States, of which comparatively few were total adhesion types, although an 0—8—8—0 type built for the Erie had a 'camelback' centre cab, about the only Mallet type so fitted. Most had pony trucks, 2—6—6—0 and 2—8—8—0, followed by 2—6—6—2 and 2—8—8—2. The Santa Fé experimented with a couple of 4—4—6—2 express locomotives with 6ft 1in driving wheels, the largest ever fitted to an articulated, while there was also a brief mania for converting conventional locomotives to Mallets by adding a front low-pressure unit and boiler

18

Simple expansion Mallets are characterised by four equal sized cylinders, as seen on No 204 of the Donna Teresa Cristina Railway, Brazil, the last of the breed in regular service anywhere in the world.
A. E. Durrant

extension, such a conversion producing the first ten-coupled articulateds, the 2—10—10—2 for the Santa Fé. The great snag with these big compound Mallets was that the leading unit had but little inherent mass, and as a result, the enormous low-pressure pistons, up to 48in diameter, thrashing backwards and forwards, caused the front unit to leap about like an elephant with St Vitus' dance, with consequent destruction of itself, the track, and anything else within striking distance. To counteract this, the Santa Fé, still trying hard, built a couple of 2—6—6—2s with flexible boilers, so that the weight of the front part, which served as a super-heater and reheater, could be mounted directly on

the forward engine unit and help to hold it down on the track. One locomotive had its two boiler halves joined together by a giant ball-and-socket joint, the diameter of the boiler, while the other had an equally giant circular, concertina-type joint. Naturally, each type, in service, filled up with red-hot cinders which ruined everything, so that eventually the Santa Fé said, 'Aw, to hell with Mallets!' and went on to develop the most gigantic 2—10—4s instead.

Other lines, eschewing the more exotic forms of Malletisation perpetrated by the Santa Fé, made a success of the type in low-speed work, until in the 1920s the superheated simple-expansion type became the accepted construction. This, with

19

improved pivots and side control, plus flat plate bearings, designed to hold the front engine unit steady, became a sophisticated motive-power unit and, with the development of the 4—6—6—4 and 4—8—8—4 types, capable of speeds up to 80mph in addition. However, by then the limit in size had been reached. The grate area on the largest types was such that, even with a four-wheel trailing truck, the front of the grate was over the coupled wheels thus severely limiting the depth of firebox and making it difficult to find room for an adequate ashpan capacity. Lima built a 2—6—6—6 type which enabled the firebox to drop below wheel level, but clearly there was not a great deal further one could go in that direction —possibly a 2—8—8—8, whose boiler might create throwever difficulties on curves, owing to its length.

The author submits that the Garratt offered a solution, and this will be dealt with in the appropriate chapter.

Chapter 2

The Garratt Locomotive

We now come to the locomotive which forms the prime subject of this work. In this chapter the development and main features of the Garratt will be discussed, together with comparisons between it and other locomotives, both conventional and articulated.

The Garratt was the brain-child of Herbert William Garratt, who was not, as is sometimes erroneously stated, an Australian, but happened to be working as an inspector for the Australian government at the time he conceived his grand idea, whose first fruit went 'down under' to Tasmania. Perhaps, therefore, it is not surprising that the Australian myth has grown up, but Garratt was an Englishman, born in 1864, who served his apprenticeship in the old North London Railway works at Bow from 1879 to 1882. He then moved to Doxford's well-known marine works at Sunderland and after acting in inspection capacities for Sir Douglas Fox and Sir Alexander Rendel went to the Central Argentine Railway in 1889, becoming locomotive superintendent there in 1892. From 1900 he then wandered to other railways—the Cuban Central, the Lagos Government, and the Lima in Peru, until 1906 when he returned to England.

However, as the story goes, he was engaged in an inspection capacity connected with some bogie or articulated vehicles for heavy artillery when the idea dawned upon him that locomotives could be built the same way. No doubt the more he thought about the idea, the better it sounded, and eventually by 1907, he had developed the idea sufficiently to apply for, and have granted, a patent.

That, of course, was the easy part. A patent is of little use until somebody is sufficiently interested to put up the money for financing and developing an idea, unless the inventor happens to be in that fortunate position himself. This was not the case with poor Garratt and he had perforce to tout his idea around the then numerous locomotive works in the country. Nobody, apparently, was interested and it would seem largely by good luck that he was at Beyer Peacock at the time when they had an enquiry for a locomotive to run on the North East Dundas Tramway in Tasmania. This line already had an articulated, or rather a semi-articulated, locomotive in the form of a Hagans 2—6—4—0T, a weird contrivance with two cylinders which drove the rigid frame set of wheels in the normal way

and the articulated set by means of a Heath Robinson arrangement of floating and pivoted rods. While admittedly it made do with but two cylinders and without flexible steampipes, the complexity of the rod work and the large numbers of pin joints must have made maintenance a nightmare and wear a chronic problem.

How Garratt interested Beyer Peacock in his idea seems not on record as he died at the early age of forty-nine, in 1913, without apparently producing anything in the way of a biography, and with comparatively few of his locomotives in service. Possibly he thought he had contributed nothing very great to locomotive engineering and simply just did not bother. Similarly, those working at and in charge of Beyer Peacock at that date, more than a working lifetime ago, have all died without committing to writing the personal record of discussions which, however imperfectly remembered, would be of the greatest interest to us today. However, the fact is that Garratt managed to interest Peacocks in his idea, and it could well be that this new and untried design was submitted to Tasmania, to a minor railway with little business potential, partly to placate Garratt and get him happily off the premises, and partly to ensure that they did not receive an order for two, odd, non-standard locomotives which have been an embarrassment to design and build.

Whether or not this was the case, the order duly arrived and the drawing office at Gorton had to get down and design the thing. These first two Garratts, before the idea had fully matured, were unlike anything else built since, being 0—4—0 + 0—4—0 with cylinders on the inner ends of the bogies, and with compound expansion, the low-pressure cylinders being on the leading units. However, they were designed, built, shipped, and presumably forgotten about. The contemporary technical and railway press appears to have taken no notice, if indeed Beyer Peacock ever sent them a handout.

Soon after, a further order was received for another engine, this time for the Darjeeling Himalaya Railway, another 2ft-gauge concern and this time the real prototype Garratt was produced with four simple-expansion cylinders positioned on the outer ends of the power bogies. Considerable interest was shown in this engine, shipped early in 1911, *The Locomotive* running an article on the railway with photograph and diagram of the Garratt which, in *The Engineer*

The front engine, boiler, and rear engine units of a Garratt as illustrated by Beyer Peacock as a sort of 'assembly kit', a form in which they were normally shipped overseas, although workshop assembly was needed before use; there could be no dockside erection and instant steaming into the interior! Beyer Peacock

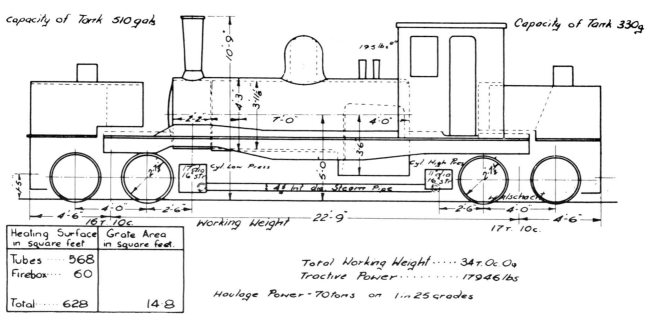

Capacity of Tank 510 gals

Capacity of Tank 330g

Heating Surface in square feet	Grate Area in square feet.
Tubes ···· 568	
Firebox ···· 60	
Total ···· 628	14·8

Working Weight ——— 22·9·

Total Working Weight ····· 34 т. 0с. 0q
Tractive Power ········· 17946 lbs
Haulage Power - 70 tons on 1 in 25 grades

The first Garratt

received an extended coverage complete with a detailed general-arrangement drawing. This was the first—and almost the last—time that Beyer Peacock let a general-arrangement drawing get out to the press. By then, they appear to have realised that they were on to a good thing and were anxious not to let possible competitors get an insight into how they dealt in detail with such vital but hidden components as pivots and flexible steam-pipe joints.

These two early Garratt designs were both of course small narrow-gauge engines, and it would appear that initially Beyer Peacock thought the potential limited to this sort of market. At any rate, they very soon arranged a licensing agreement with the Société Anonyme de Saint Léonard of Liège in Belgium, probably with the idea of breaking into the market for small 0—4—4—0T Mallets which was substantial at that time.

However, it was not the European market that St Léonard broke into, but the African. Today, we tend to associate the Garratt with Africa, which is only right, as more Garratts went to Africa than to all the rest of the world put together, while of surviving Garratts, an even greater proportion live on that continent. Yet it was not Beyer Peacock with their semi-captive British Colonial market that reached there first. The initial BP deliveries to Africa were for the South African Railways in 1919, although admittedly the order had been placed in 1914 and delayed by the war. But even so—the Belgians preceded them! The first delivery, in 1911, comprised four dinky little 0—4—0 + 0—4—0 Garratts for the 600mm-gauge Chemins de fer Vicinaux du Mayumbe in the Belgian Congo, these 23½ ton

locomotives being the smallest Garratts ever built apart from models and miniatures. In the same year, an 0—6—0 + 0—6—0 for the 750mm-gauge Compagnie du Chemins de fer du Congo was supplied, and this proved to be the prototype for a substantial number of similar locomotives. Then in 1912, the Société Anonyme des Mines du Zaccar in Algeria, again 750mm gauge, took delivery of an 0—4—0 + 0—4—0 Garratt of similar appearance to the Mayumbe minis, but larger.

Meanwhile, Beyer Peacock were really selling Garratts, and had produced a brochure extolling the virtues of the type. They still thought of it as a heavy-duty freight locomotive only, and this early publication shows photographs of the Dundas Tram and Darjeeling Garratts, the only ones built at the time. However, an artist's impression depicts an 0—6—0 + 0—6—0, standard gauge, blasting through rugged country, with a 1 in 25 gradient post beside the track, and trailing a load of bogie wagons loaded with some kind of mineral, presumably coal. A diagram also is shown of this locomotive which with an 18-ton axle load could have a tractive effort of 50,000lb. Furthermore, another diagram shows, also standard gauge, and within the British loading gauge, an 0—8—0 + 0—8—0 Garratt with 60sq ft of grate area, and 72,000lb tractive effort. Here Peacocks were evidently getting down to some serious thinking, and while no 0—8—0 + 0—8—0 Garratt was ever built, the design closely foreshadowed in size and power, the 2—8—0 + 0—8—2 eventually supplied to the LNER.

Clearly by now it was realised that the Garratt had something over the other articulated types, and it is as well here, perhaps a few pages

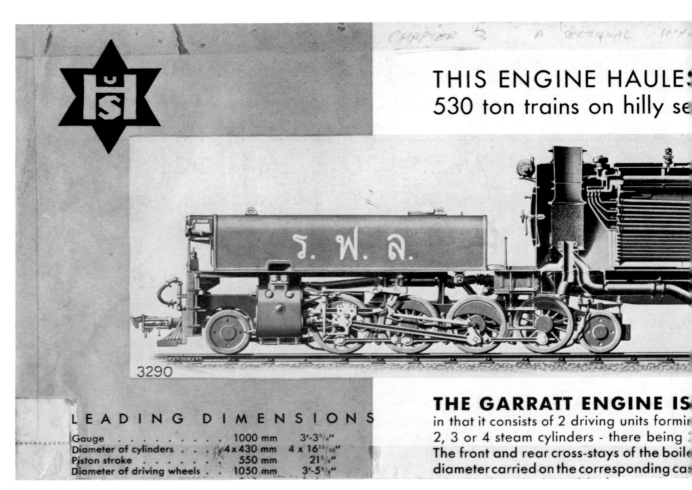

THIS ENGINE HAULE
530 ton trains on hilly se

THE GARRATT ENGINE IS
in that it consists of 2 driving units formir
2, 3 or 4 steam cylinders - there being
The front and rear cross-stays of the boile
diameter carried on the corresponding ca

LEADING DIMENSIONS

Gauge	1000 mm	3'-3⁵/₈"
Diameter of cylinders	4 x 430 mm	4 x 16¹⁵/₁₆"
Piston stroke	550 mm	21⁵/₈"
Diameter of driving wheels	1050 mm	3'-5³/₈"

Beyer Peacock, as major patentees, were naturally reluctant to publish inside details of their Garratts. No such inhibitions were held by Henschel, who

published this section of a Siamese Garratt to show potential customers that they really knew how the thing worked! Henschel & Sohn

belatedly, to describe a Garratt and its advantages over its competitors. Fundamentally, the Garratt is of a simple principle, and it comprises two engine units, which may be of any type or wheel arrangement, the leading one carrying the main water tank while the hind unit carries the fuel bunker plus a lesser supply of water. Slung between, and pivoted to both, is the boiler unit, which carries the boiler and the cab.

Such a system has many advantages, the first being that the design is, as it were, spacious, and there is plenty of room for everything.

The engine units may be of any desired or convenient wheel arrangement, and the same lack of limitation applies to the cylinders. The driving wheels, not being under the boiler or firebox, are not restricted in diameter, as was often the case with the earlier types of articulated locomotives. Furthermore, having a tank placed directly upon it, each power unit has a greater inherent mass, which makes for a better riding unit.

As for the boiler, again, not being over the wheels or chassis, the size is restricted only by the loading gauge, a limit rarely reached, and in particular, the firebox can be made of adequate depth, and have slung under it an ample ashpan.

The firebox can be a simple rectangular box, there being no need to provide an expensive combustion chamber of complicated shape as the deep firebox provides all the volume required for combustion. Similarly, the boiler barrel tends to adopt the best shape for free steaming, ie short and of large diameter.

While the Garratt performs the same basic function as other articulated types, it does it more effectively. Taking the two main functions of an articulated, that of spreading the weight over numerous axles, and of providing greater flexibility on curves, the Garratt can be seen to do this with particular efficiency. Spreading of the weight is achieved not only by increasing the number of axles, but also by dividing them into two distinct groups, separated by a considerable gap. Thus where track limitations arise from weak bridges as well as light rails, the Garratt may be technically superior on a weight per foot length basis, all other things being equal, simply because only one unit is on a span at one time, whereas on other articulateds the weight, while spread over numerous axles, is still concentrated over a comparatively short wheelbase.

Turning to the question of flexibility, the

P

ns with long gradients of 1:60 to 1:42

ARTICULATED ENGINE

exible connection with a rigid frame on which the boiler is supported. Each driving unit comprises
e present instance - with an equivalent number of driving gears of the standard locomotive type.
e are each fitted with a short cylindrical pivot pointing downward and engaging in sockets of ample
cross-members of the driving bogie frames. The steam from the regulator is led through separate main

Garratt is comparable in size with a main-line Mallet tender engine, and one can see that, for example, a 2—6—6—2 Mallet with an eight-wheel tender will provide an adequate freight engine, rough riding, and with limited wheel diameter. The same number of wheels, coupled and uncoupled, however, will support a 4—6—2 + 2—6—4 Garratt. In other words, a double Pacific which will not only have the same riding and tracking qualities of a Pacific but can, if desired, have as large driving wheels and also as great a capacity for heavy haulage as the Mallet. Such a machine is in theory—and in practice—the operating man's dream.

Compared with other articulated types, the Garratt has no serious overhang problems, and in fact the greatest throwover occurs at the centre of the boiler unit, which being pivot-supported at both ends remains a stable unit, unlike say the overhung front on the Mallet or the tanks on the 'Modified Fairlie'. Even when empty, the weight of the tanks themselves is sufficient to assist in holding the engine units down. Again, as pointed out, compared with a Mallet tender engine, the transfer of the tender wheels to act as bogies with the Garratt is in itself a steadying influence. This

brings us to a criticism which has sometimes been levelled at the Garratt, that of the diminution of adhesion weight as fuel and water supplies are used up. That this phenomenon occurs cannot be denied, but it is no more serious than with a normal tank engine, while with its multiplicity of driving wheels, the Garratt has generally been given an ample adhesion factor to compensate for this. It is significant that this criticism came mainly from the USA, where the railways were not great users of tank engines and never put a Garratt into service, although it was seriously considered.

One of the important features of the Garratt, which it shared with the Kitson-Meyer, was that of enabling the boiler to be of optimum proportions, ie of large diameter and with short tube length, and having a deep firebox giving ample volume for combustion. Equally, there is plenty of room underneath for a capacious ashpan, a very necessary feature in some of the areas where Garratts have been put to work, where coal of up to 40 per cent ash content has been supplied.

Beyer Peacock's catalogues and brochures on the Garratt have always stressed that the firebox can be built up to a size where it fits the loading gauge like a hand inside a glove, but this is not strictly true, and there are definite limitations. These concern the components which have to be got round the firebox somehow or other, and they are surprisingly numerous and occasionally bulky. The list is as follows:

Main steam pipes to rear unit
Exhaust steam pipes from rear unit
Brake pipes between units
Tank balancing pipes between units
Steam heating pipes (if any) between units
Reverse gear to front unit (hand reverse)
Reverse gear to rear unit (power reverse)
Cylinder cock gear to front unit
Electric light conduit (if applicable)

Many of these components are comparatively small, and easily accommodated on the boiler frame, but such items as the steam and exhaust pipes are not so easily led round the firebox. Obviously, also, the larger the locomotive the larger the firebox and the larger the steam and exhaust pipes, thus accentuating the problem. The remedy was usually to run these pipes underneath the firebox, which at best is a compromise, as it meant sacrificing valuable ashpan capacity which, with a large locomotive, would also be at a premium. This limitation never became an insuperable problem, but had a very large Garratt ever been proposed for say, the British loading gauge, the routeing of these pipes around the firebox would undoubtedly have become the ultimate limiting factor.

The layout of the Garratt was such that it lent itself particularly well to standardisation of cylinders, wheels, motion, etc, with existing locomotives on a railway, and this was often incorporated in a design, although not so frequently as might be expected. Possibly, early results with the undershod LMS efforts gave Peacocks a strong lever in persuading a railway to accept a completely new design. Similarly, the Garratt to a greater extent than the other types, lent itself easily to the conversion of two existing locomotives into one Garratt. Such conversions, both to and from the Mallet type, were once rife within the USA but surprisingly, conversion from conventional to Garratt never got past the proposal stages, while there is but one case of an unsatisfactory Garratt being broken down into normal locomotives.

Compound propulsion has been tried twice, surprisingly with the high- and low-pressure cylinders on separate units. While this gave, in the form of the connecting pipe, the high receiver volume as advocated by Chapelon, a long pipe was probably more effective as a condenser than as a receiver. The more obvious and sensible arrangement, where each engine unit is a self-contained compound, was never actually used.

Garratts with turbines and also with condensers have been patented, but never, as far as the author is aware, seriously proposed. The Garratt would appear to offer a particularly favourable condition for a condensing locomotive, yet the only condensers of recent build, the SAR 25 class, were conventional engines, notwithstanding that railway's satisfactory experience with Garratts, some of which were under construction at the same time. The majority of Garratts built have used straightforward two-cylinder simple-expansion power units, and apart from the odd compounds mentioned, there have been two designs with three-, and one with four-cylinder power units. A type which was proposed and patented in the 1920s was the 'Super Garratt' or 'Mallet Garratt', in which each engine unit was subdivided into two, on the same principle as the Mallet. Fortunately for the reputation of Beyer Peacock, this monstrosity never got off the drawing-board, although seriously considered by the South African Railways and also for use in the USA.

The USA proposal, which, like the SAR one, was of the 2—6—6—2 + 2—6—6—2 type, was of particular interest, inasmuch as it invalidated the usual American excuse that the Garratt was unsuitable for conditions in USA, due to its limited water and coal capacity. It is interesting thus to compare its vital statistics with the two largest locomotives then operating in the USA, the Virginian 2—10—10—2 Mallet and the Erie 2—8—8—8—2 'Triplex', which was virtually a Mallet with a steam tender. The proposed Garratt substantially exceeds the two existing locomotives in all dimensions and capacities without, however, exceeding the then stipulated axle load of 67,200lb. The grate area and tractive effort are greater than the Union Pacific 'Big Boy' 4—8—8—4, the ultimate world's largest, and given another twenty years' development, there is no doubt that a Garratt of substantially greater capacity than a 'Big Boy' was perfectly feasible, furthermore, without the cramped conditions inherent in the placing of a large firebox over the 5ft 7in wheels of the Mallet. A suitable wheel arrangement for such a large USA Garratt for general use, could have been a 4—10—4 + 4—10—4, while the Union Pacific with its successful operation of 4—12—2s might even have gone in for a 4—12—4 + 4—12—4. The table below gives relevant dimensions of the proposed Garratt and the other locomotives mentioned.

The South African 'Super Garratt' was a much more modest affair, not as big even as the subsequent 'GL' class, although admittedly on a 13 ton axle load. Both 'Super Garratt' designs included the coal bunker on the boiler frame, in order to apply a mechanical stoker without recourse to

The Beyer Peacock patent rotary coal bunker, open and closed, as applied to the LMS Garratts. Although advertised as being equally applicable to 'straight' locomotives, it was actually applied only to Garratts. Beyer Peacock

Railway	(Garratt)	Virginian	Erie	Union Pacific
TYPE	2-6-6-2+ 2-6-6-2	2-10-10-2	2-8-8-8-2	4-8-8-4
Tractive effort (85%) lb	203,000	147,200	160,000	135,375
Grate area sq ft	160·0	108·7	90·0	150·3
Total weight lb	1032,000	898,300	853,050	1120,000
Adhesion weight lb	808,000	617,000	761,600	545,000
Coal (US tons)	18	12	16	28
Water (US gals)	19,200	13,000	10,000	25,000

flexible connections between bunker and firebox. This feature was also built into the New Zealand Garratts, and of course the 'Union Garratts' for the SAR. However, it was soon realised that a stoker which could function successfully over the bucking and swaying connection between a normal locomotive and its tender, would do so even better across the disciplined joint of a Garratt, and this feature was then discontinued.

The Garratt, at various times, received most of the modern aids to efficiency. Poppet valves, roller bearings on both axleboxes and crankpins, cast-steel beds, thermic syphons, and feedwater heaters, to mention the principal items, have all been applied, while superheaters were almost universal. Of those features which have proved themselves elsewhere, only all-welded boilers and 'Boxpok' driving wheels seem missing. Modern exhaust arrangements, such as the 'Kylchap', were applied to but a few Garratts when new, but recently a good number have been fitted with Giesl ejectors, particularly on the East African Railways.

Garratts have been built to burn wood, coal, or oil, with evident success in each case, but none have ever been fitted for burning pulverised coal. Apart from mechanical stokers, coal pushers have been fitted on certain large hand-fired types, while another ingenious device, patented by Beyer Peacock, was their rotary bunker. This consisted of a conical shaped bunker, pivoted at each end and rotated by a small steam engine, the movement bringing the coal forward to the shovel plate. The bunker was filled through small hatches which had to be battened down, consuming time at the running sheds. The whole ensemble was as complex as a full mechanical stoker, without being so effective, and was fitted, rather uncharacteristically, to the Midland-inspired Garratts of the LMS and, more predictably, to the gadget-infested express locomotives built in France for Algeria. In service the space under the revolving bunkers gradually became filled with coal spilt while loading, until the whole thing jammed solid.

As might be expected, with two sets of valve gear to operate, a form of power reverse was developed by Beyer Peacock, and known as the Hadfield reverse after its designer. It comprises a power cylinder, operable either by steam or air pressure, and a cataract cylinder filled with oil which maintains the gear in the required position without creep. In principle, it is similar to other power gears, but attention to detail has perfected a trouble-free device which has been applied to most large modern Garratts.

Walschaerts valve gear has been applied to the great bulk of Garratts built, plus a variety of types of poppet valves, some driven by Walschaerts gear and others by rotary motion. Surprisingly, there have not been even the odd examples with Stephenson gear, even the few early types with slide valves having Walschaerts motion. The earlier Garratts had their valve gear arranged, predictably, so that when the locomotive was proceeding chimney first, the leading unit was in forward gear and the rear in reverse, with the radius rods at the lower and upper sectors of the link respectively. Later examples, however, had this rearranged so that both sets of motion were lowered for chimney-first working and vice versa.

There now remains to be exploded a myth about Garratts which has been perpetuated by many, including even eminent engineers who ought to have known better! The myth is that the two sets of motion on a Garratt allegedly get 'in step' once the locomotive is under way. Those familiar with Garratts know, of course, that this is utter nonsense, happening only occasionally by coincidence. The two units are not coupled in any way, and in fact the wheels of each revolve freely and independently of one another. The origin of the myth appears to stem from the older Garratts with Z shaped steam ports, and inadequate, short lap, valves. Once under way, the muffled exhaust from the rear unit became quite 'lost' in the long length of exhaust pipe, so that only the exhaust from the forward unit could be heard at all distinctly. By comparison, modern Garratts such as the SAR GMAM, or NSW AD60 classes, where the exhaust beat from each unit comes through loud and clear, can be heard to wander in and out of synchronisation continuously, as might be expected.

Apart from variation due to wheel slip, or the differential tracking of front and rear units on curves, there is a very simple engineering explanation for the wide range of unsynchronisation that may be heard by Garratt observers, and that is that the mean wheel diameter on one unit is unlikely to be the same as on the other. Anybody familiar with mechanical engineering will know that nothing can be made to an exact size; components are manufactured to within a plus or minus tolerance. This, of course, is very much so with locomotive driving and coupled wheels, and it is relevant to quote from South African Railways code of practice, as being the largest users of Garratts, and therefore typical:
Clause 6.2.1. 'The difference in diameter between any two wheels in the same set of coupled wheels is not to exceed 0·031in'.
Clause 6.3.1.3. 'The difference between the average diameter of the coupled wheels of one unit and the corresponding dimension for the other unit of a Garratt locomotive must not exceed 1in'.

In other words, one set of wheels may be as much as an inch smaller than the other. For a normal Garratt with two-cylinder units, one eighth of a revolution relative movement will bring the two units totally out of step, and another eighth will bring them actually 90 degrees out of step, but audibly back into step. For a locomotive with a nominal wheel diameter of 4ft 6in (1372mm), but one set ¼in (6mm) smaller than the other, the two units will become audibly completely out of phase in 27 revolutions, about 380ft (116m), and will re-synchronise in the same distance, assuming no wheelslip. With the maximum difference in wheel diameter permitted in the SAR code, these phenomena will occur in one quarter of those distances. For those readers of this book who are unable to go out and hear for themselves, there are now several Australian and South African recordings available, clearly demonstrating the fact that Garratts do *not* in fact tend to synchronise.

*A one-piece cast steel bed frame as supplied to the
South African Railways final Garratt classes.*
General Steel Castings Inc

Some comparisons between Garratts and either conventional or Mallet locomotives are not out of place to end this chapter, and two railways have been chosen to illustrate certain points. The first is the classic South African case, where an MH class 2—6—6—2 Mallet is compared with a GA 2—6—0 + 0—6—2 Garratt, both types being similar in grate area and tractive effort. The additional dead weight of the Mallet with its tender is substantial; eleven tons of this are accounted for by the empty boiler alone, as shown in the accompanying table. The whole of the Garratt heating surface is within 11ft 8in of the rear tubeplate, whereas only half that of the Mallet is so close to the fire. The table shows the difference clearly.

Thus, other things being virtually equal, the Garratt was 45·7 tons lighter than the equivalent Mallet, this representing the additional load which can be hauled, or about 10 per cent more

train on a 1 in 40 gradient. Additionally, the Garratt showed coal and water savings when hauling test loads of around 1000 tons over the 1 in 65 gradients between Estcourt and Stockton.

A later comparison may be made between conventional and Garratt types on the same railway, where from 1929 to 1936 the CME, one A. G. Watson, strongly opposed the use of articulated locomotives, probably a backlash from his predecessor, from whom he inherited too diverse a variety of such motive power. Greater power was needed on branch lines laid with 60lb rail, for which the most powerful non-articulated locomotives available were the 19th classes, having 31,850lb tractive effort at 75 per cent boiler pressure. Watson used his 15E boiler, spread over an additional axle to give a 2—10—4 design, class 21, with 43,700lb tractive effort, a 37 per cent increase over the 19 class with an even greater increase in boiler capacity. However, his

WHOLE LOCOMOTIVE			BOILER ONLY		
Type	Mallet 2·6·6·2	Garratt 2·6·0+ 0·6·2	Class	MH	GA
Class	MH	GA	Grate area (sq ft)	53·2	51·8
Tractive effort (lb)	48370	47390	Maximum inside diameter	6′ 2½″	6′ 9″
Maximum axle load (tons)	18·2	17·8	Length between tubeplates	22′ 0″	11′ 8¼″
Total weight working order (tons)	179·6	133·9	Firebox volume (cu ft)	327	311
Adhesion weight working order (tons)	105·5	105·2	Firebox heating surface (sq ft)	250	211·3
Coal capacity (tons)	10	9	Tube heating surface (sq ft)	2961	2343·2
Water capacity (gal)	4250	4500	Superheating surface (sq ft)	616	526·5
Length over buffers	79′ 15″	65′ 6″	Weight empty (tons)	35·54	24·5

	WHOLE LOCOMOTIVE			BOILER ONLY		
Type	2-10-4	Garratt 4-8-2+ 2-8-4	Class		21	GM
Class	21	GM	Grate area (sq ft)		62·5	63·6
Tractive effort 75% (lb)	43700	60700	Maximum inside diameter		6' 5¾"	7' 1½"
Maximum axle load (tons)	14·95	15·0	Length between tubeplates		22' 6"	13' 6½"
Total weight working order (tons)	172·4	174·3*	Firebox heating surface (sq ft)		232	279
Adhesion weight working order	72·9	115·1	Tube heating surface (sq ft)		3168	2771
Coal capacity (tons)	10	10	Superheating surface (sq ft)		676	770
Water capacity (gal)	5587	1600*	Weight empty (tons)		34·75	31·5
Length over buffers	76' 10"	93' 4½"	Evaporation lb/hr		42000	47000

*Plus auxiliary water tank—weight 51 tons capacity 6810 gal

successor, W. A. J. Day, was not so biassed against articulateds, and introduced the GM class Garratt having 60,700lb tractive effort, nearly double that of the 19th class, and 39 per cent more than the ten-coupled engine. If the proof of the pudding can be said to be in the eating, the Garratt's superiority can be confirmed by the fact that the 21 class was never multiplied, whereas the GM class was developed into the GMA and GMAM classes, making a total of 136 Garratts having the same basic dimensions and haulage capacity.

The other two examples come from Spain, which is probably the only other country in the world to operate both conventional and Garratt locomotives of similar power, to suit different conditions of track. Like the South African examples, the feature which stands out clearly is that while the conventional locomotives have approached the maximum size permitted by weight and other limitations, the Garratt provides a similar capacity on a far more light-footed machine, and could be developed to provide substantially greater power.

These figures, from the official RENFE sources, compute the tractive effort at 65 per cent boiler pressure, and the horsepower figures are presumably indicated.

RENFE—GARRATT AND CONVENTIONAL LOCOMOTIVES

Class	241.2201	462.0401 4-6-2+	151.3101	282.0401 2-8-2+
Type	4-8-2	2-6-4	2-10-2	2-8-2
Duties	Express	Express	Freight	Freight
Total weight (tonnes)	204·0	184·0	213·2	161·5
Adhesion weight (tonnes)	84·0	93·0	105·1	108·0
Max axle load (tonnes)	21·0	15·3	21·0	13·5
Grate area (sq metres)	5·3	4·9	5·3	4·2
Tractive effort (kg)	17690	18540	25000	22200
Horsepower	2700	2380	2700	2000

Garratt Maintenance

It has been fashionable in some circles to condemn the Garratt as being 'heavy on maintenance', an allegation which is meaningless without being placed in perspective. For example, on South African Railways, maintenance costs are recorded in cents per kilometre, an accounting statistic which ignores such important factors as the work performed by the locomotive, or the type of service used on. Thus, for secondary lines, the GMAM Garratt was 'heavy' at 86 cents/km compared with the 19D at 61c/km, ignoring the fact that *two* 19D are needed to haul the Garratt's load, making 122c/km if equated to haulage capacity instead of unit locomotives. Similarly, Garratts tend to be used on mountainous routes where speeds are low, making the denominator of the cost equation artificially low. Thus, the 86c/km for the GMAM sounded remarkably high compared with a 25NC's 37c/km, mainly because the Class 25 4—8—4 tender engines were largely working on routes having easier gradients and often double track also, permitting higher speeds, and thus more kilometres per unit time. It is probably true to say that where traffic can be handled by a single conventional locomotive, this will be more economical than using an unnecessary articulated design, but where two unarticulated are required, a single Garratt will be more economical.

Having compared the Garratt principle with conventional locomotives and with other articulated types the remaining chapters are concerned with the detail of Garratt designs throughout the world, their generation, distribution and decline in face of dieselisation and electrification.

Europe

Although the Garratt was evolved in Europe, and most were built in that continent, few European countries took advantage of the locomotives' capabilities. Conditions particularly favourable to Garratt operation: steep gradients, sinuous single track, and restricted axle loads were found in Scandinavia, South Eastern Europe, and the Iberian peninsular. Of these, only the latter became a Garratt user while other spheres of operation were in unexpected places.

Britain

The biggest pocket of Garratts in Europe was surprisingly, in Great Britain, which was perhaps the most unlikely place of all. A land where a freight train was a string of unbraked match-boxes-on-wheels, crawling along at a snail's pace, would hardly seem the place for a machine such as a Garratt. However, there were parts where really hard work had to be done, although few of these ever saw a Garratt.

The first Garratt proposal seems to have come from the Great Central Railway about 1910, for a banking engine on the Worsborough incline on the Barnsley-Penistone direct freight line. With the GC's Gorton 'tank', as the works was known, just across the line from Beyer Peacock's works, only two minutes walk over the wooden footbridge which spanned the track, it is hardly surprising that word of the new type soon reached the ears of the GC men. Whether this was done officially or came about over an ale in a local pub is not now known, but the proposal was for a machine with two eight-coupled units standard with Robinson's tender engines. The scheme hung about for a long time, and was delayed by the war, after which it was resuscitated just before the grouping of the railways. At grouping, Gresley became the CME of the new London & North Eastern Railway and, no doubt to his surprise, he found that he had a Garratt proposal on his hands. That a Garratt, or for that matter any sort of articulated locomotive, was not Gresley's idea of how a locomotive should be engineered was made quite clear when he spoke at the Institution of Locomotive Engineers meeting at Leeds in 1920, expressing relief that conditions in Britain made articulateds unnecessary. That, however, was before he inherited the Great Central and it was not long after grouping when the Garratt proposal was taken out, dusted, re-

schemed with three-cylinder power units standard with Gresley's Great Northern 2—8—0s and an order placed upon Beyer Peacock for No 2395, Class U1, which was delivered in 1925. As the largest locomotive built for Great Britain, both at that time and indeed subsequently, it was exhibited at the centenary celebrations of the Stockton & Darlington Railway, held in 1925, and was one of the many locomotives which held a run-past for the benefit of those visiting.

Afterwards it assumed its duties at Worsboro', and for a quarter of a century shuttled up and down those 2½ miles of line, rather off the beaten track, and unseen by the majority of photographers. Indeed, the author has been unable to trace any good photographs of it at work there. The normal arrangement was for a coal train to arrive with an 'O4' class 2—8—0 hauling, whereupon the Garratt plus another 'O4' would bank the train up the 1 in 40 incline, the train load being 1200 tons, which should not have needed so much power except for the fact that colliery subsidences caused the gradients to vary so that sections were much steeper than the nominal.

After the war, in March 1949, when the line was electrified, the 'U1' was transferred to the Lickey incline at Bromsgrove, again for banking up the 1 in 37¾ gradient to Blackwell. In November 1950 it returned to the Eastern Region and was stored. During April 1951 consideration was given to fitting it with the mechanical stoker from the Southern 'Merchant Navy', but this was found impracticable, so conversion to oil burning was authorised and completed in December 1952. Experiments with various flame pans were carried out sporadically until a steaming rate of 35,000lb/hr was achieved, after which, in June 1955 it returned to Bromsgrove for further banking duties. However, it was never popular on this job, and due to the difficulty of judging the distance from the cab to the front buffer beam, generally banked cab first, which meant that in order to maintain an adequate depth of water over the firebox crownplate the boiler was generally over-full of water, with resultant priming. The boiler being life-expired in November 1955, the locomotive was withdrawn from service, and subsequently scrapped.

The LNER 'U1' was among the first eight-coupled Garratts built, and the first to have three cylinders on each unit. The valves of the centre cylinders were operated by Gresley's conjugated

31

*Former LNER class U1 Garratt, BR No 69999, banks
a short freight, hauled by a Midland 'Big goods'
0—6—0, up the Lickey incline.* British Railways

gear, the working parts of each unit being entirely standard with his 'O2' class 2—8—0. Otherwise, the locomotive had no features of particular technical interest, and the boiler was, as one might expect, a large round-topped affair which suited the design policies of both Gresley and Beyer Peacock.

Although the first envisaged, the LNER 'U1' was not the first to run in Great Britain, this honour belonging to a little industrial 0—4—0 + 0—4—0 which Beyer Peacock turned out in 1924 for Vivian & Sons Ltd of Hafod, Swansea. The problem here was to obtain a powerful locomotive capable of surmounting a 1 in 20 gradient and traversing a curve of 97ft radius, with loads up to 168 tons. This the little Garratt performed ably and its success made it the forerunner of further industrial Garratts. The original locomotive changed owners when the British Copper Manufacturers Ltd took Vivians over, and again when they were in turn absorbed by Imperial Chemical Industries, who finally transferred the locomotive to their Billingham works, where it was scrapped.

Further industrial Garratts to the same design as the original were supplied in 1931 to the Sneyd Collieries, Burslem, Stoke-on-Trent, to Guest,

Keen & Baldwins, Cardiff works, in 1934, and to the Baddesley Colliery, near Atherstone, Warwickshire, in 1937, this last also being the last in service, finally ceasing work in 1965.

These industrial Garratts were built as most industrial locomotives, unsuperheated, and with slide-valve cylinders driven by Walschaerts gear. Plate frames were used, together with Belpaire boilers, and all had the square-cornered rectangular tanks typical of the earlier Garratts.

Next in Britain were the 2—6—0 + 0—6—2 supplied to the London Midland & Scottish Railway, which at the time was suffering from the perpetuation of the small-engine policy pursued by its largest constituent, the former Midland Railway. This policy also manifested itself in the blind standardisation of undersized axleboxes from the pairs of 0—6—0 tender engines which the Garratts replaced and also the use of short-lap valve gear largely standard with the Somerset & Dorset 2—8—0s. The story is very well told by E. S. Cox in his excellent book *Locomotive Panorama*, and it is sufficient to say here that while the LMS Garratts were not as good as they might have been, they at least performed the work of two 0—6—0s with a saving of one engine crew. Beyer Peacock claimed a 15-20 per cent coal

Garratts galore at New Hanover. Double-headed Garratts were the normal power on South African Railways Greytown branch; here a GF plus GMAM combination rolls into the passing loop while a pair of GMAMs, having watered, await the right away with a load for Pietermaritzburg.   A. E. Durrant

(above)   On the Sierra Menera railway in Spain,
Garratt No 502 approaches Puerto del Escandon
hauling a load of iron ore, and banked by an
0—6—6—0 compound Mallet.   A. C. Sterndale

(below)   Broad gauge, English coaches, and tropical
background provide the setting for Sri Lanka's class
C1A Garratt No 345 as it prepares to leave Kandy.
R. A. Kingsford-Smith

saving compared with the 0—6—0s, a claim which Cox refutes. In all probability the Garratts did save coal when new, but settled down to the standard level of consumption when run into normal worn condition. The amount of tractive effort built into these engines with their 21 ton axle load—incidentally the highest axle load of any Garratt built—was very low and indeed the size of boiler plus the tractive effort could have been easily built into a large 2—8—0 with 21 ton axle load.

Three of these Garratts were built in 1927 and put to work on coal trains from Toton Yard (near Nottingham) to Brent Yard, Cricklewood (in North West London), a route 126½ miles long with an undulating profile, but no gradient steeper than 1 in 132, upon which they hauled 1500 tons. These three, Nos 4997—99, were built to a height of only 12ft 9in, and in addition to the features already mentioned, had plate frames, Belpaire fireboxes, superheaters, and were generally given the Fowler LMS look by the fitting of a suitable chimney and dome. Although intended for mineral trains, which were of course unbraked, these initial three engines included vacuum brake equipment although retaining three-link couplings. Bogie brakes were also fitted.

(above) The LMS Garratts were inherently unsuitable for fast running, due to poor valve events and undersized bearings, despite which, optimistic tests were conducted. No 4999, as first built, with short chimney and normal coal bunker, sports express headlights on this trial run with empty stock and dynamometer car, about 1930.   F. G. Carrier

(below) In final form, with British Railways' number, taller chimney, rotary bunker, and regulation layer of grime, ex-LMS Garratt No 47974 clanks along the Midland main line with unbraked low capacity coal trucks.   British Railways, LMR

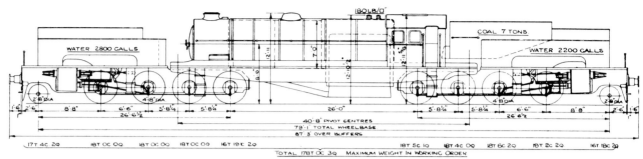

LNER 2—8—0 + 0—8—2 Garratt locomotive, type U—1.

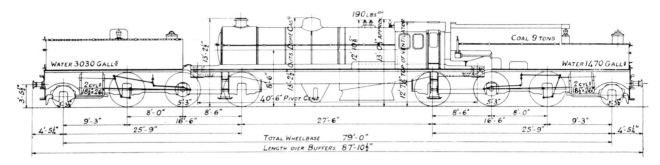

LMS 2—6—0 + 0—6—2 Nos 4967—96 as built.

In 1930 a further thirty locomotives were supplied, Nos 4967—96, and these differed in having taller chimneys and domes, bringing the overall height to 13ft 2½in. The tanks and bunkers were of greater capacity and 'Trick' piston valves with double exhaust ports were fitted. To ease the fireman's burden, coal pushers were included but these were apparently inadequate, and eventually Beyer Peacock's rotary bunker was fitted to all except 4998—99.

The Garratts were used mainly on the coal trains from Toton to Brent, and were largely stationed at Toton and Wellingborough. As from about 1935, some were stationed at Hasland and Westhouses, both near Chesterfield, and from these sheds they tended to operate over the Hope Valley line and also as far north as York.

No 4984 was temporarily fitted with vacuum brakes and used on trial runs with passenger stock, as a preliminary to the proposed building of express passenger Garratts.

In 1938—9 they were renumbered 7967—99, and later in 1948 47967—99 under the British Railways scheme. At least two attempts were made to use them as bankers on the Lickey incline, but they were no more successful on this than the LNER Garratt. From time to time they wandered down to Gloucester or Bristol over this line, necessitating a return up the Lickey, and one memorable photograph shows a short train hauled by an LMS and banked by the LNER Garratt, which had somehow managed to stall, and was being rescued by the Lickey banker

0—10—0 bringing up the rear!

On both the main line and these occasional forays they were eventually replaced by Riddles' astounding Class 9 2—10—0. Commencing with 47985/90 in June 1953 they were withdrawn, the last survivor being 47994 in April 1958.

The LMS from time to time considered the extended use of Garratts, and for details of these one should refer again to Cox's *Locomotive Panorama*. Basically there was a 4—4—2 + 2—4—4 with three-cylinder compound power units, standard with the Midland compounds, and Beyer Peacock's counter-proposal, which was a 4—6—2 + 2—6—4 rather like the first Algerian Garratt. There were, of course, earlier schemes for those actually built and, shortly after the second world war, schemes for further 4—6—2 + 2—6—4s with different wheel diameters for freight and passenger work.

None of these, however, came to fruition, but it is interesting to speculate upon what could be done with a Garratt within the British Railways L2 loading gauge. Using a boiler with 100sq ft of grate area, and 4—10—2 power units with 5ft 6in wheels and 21in × 34in cylinders, 265lb pressure, and a 21 ton axle load, a mixed traffic locomotive capable of exerting 102,345lb tractive effort and developing 6000ihp would result. This is far ahead of any locomotive, steam, electric, or diesel ever used or even thought of by British Railways, and it shows that steam power is far from having been developed to its ultimate potential.

Building details of British Garratts are:

Industrial Garratt in the snow. Britain's last Garratt in regular operation is shown leaving Atherstone Wharf for Baddesley Colliery on a January morning.

This locomotive is now preserved on a tourist site, but seems unlikely ever to work hard again.
A. E. Durrant

Railway	Numbers/ Names	Beyer Peacock Nos	Dates
Vivian/Brit Copper/ICI	10/23	6172	1924
LNER/BR	2395/9999/69999	6209	1925
LMS/BR	4997-9/7997-9/47997-9	6325-27	1927
LMS/BR	4967-96/7967-96/ 47967-96	6648-77	1930
Sneyd Colly	3	6729	1931
Baldwin-British	12	6779	1934
Baddesley Colly	*William Francis*	6841	1937

Spain

The other European country using a significant number of Garratts was Spain where, as early as 1922, the metre gauge FC Catalanes took delivery of four 2—6—0 + 0—6—2 locomotives from the Societé St Léonard of Liége. Numbered 101—104, they were superheated, piston-valve jobs with inside frames. A Belpaire firebox was provided and the steampipe connection from the dome to the superheater header was outside the boiler barrel, as on certain French locomotives. An unusual and distinctive feature was the cylindrical front tank. A further four locomotives of the same design, Nos 105—108, were supplied in 1925 and the Garratts worked the heavy freight traffic over the unelectrified sections of the line until the 1950s when they were gradually replaced by diesels. However, three still remained in store at Sallent in early 1967, but seemed unlikely ever to be steamed again. Building details were:

Railway Numbers	St Léonard Nos	Dates
101—104	1960—1963	1922
105—108	2035—2038	1925

Various railways introduced Garratts about 1930, ranging from the Rio Tinto in the south to the F.C. de La Robla in the north. The Rio Tinto

Catalan Railways Garratt No 101 poses in Martorell shed yard in 1961.   R. Payne

is a 3ft 6in-gauge railway, and the two 2—6—2 + 2—6—2 supplied by Beyer Peacock, running numbers 145 and 146, were of the same design as those supplied earlier for industrial work in South Africa, and details of them will be found in Chapter 8. The line, which is 52 miles long, with a maximum gradient of 1 in 50, was built for hauling pyrites and sulphur from the inland Rio Tinto mines to the port of Huelva, from where the minerals were shipped. The loads handled were up to 2000 tons loaded, downhill, and 550 tons of empties uphill. By 1970 both locomotives had been out of service for a number of years, being replaced by diesels, although the railway still operated steam on lighter duties. Beyer Peacock's numbers were 6560 and 6561, dated 1930.

The La Robla locomotives, like the other Spanish narrow-gauge examples, were of metre gauge. These were designed by Hanomag, who built the first two, the remaining pair being made to the same drawings by Babcock and Wilcox in Bilbao. The design comprised a 2—6—2 + 2—6—2 wheel arrangement, rather long and drawn out, and was a straightforward superheated simple job. In appearance they have some resemblance to the South African Railways GF class, built earlier by Hanomag, and to assist in negotiating sharp curves, the centre tyres of each unit were flangeless, the drive being on the inner coupled axles. As was then the La Robla practice, they were named as follows:

No	Name	Builder, No & Date	
80	*Venancio de Echeverria*	Hanomag	10646/29
81	*Jose J. de Ampuero*	,,	10647/29
82	*Enrique de Borda*	Babcock	421/31
83	*Jose Ma. de Basterra*	,,	422/31

The whole class has been out of service for some years and has now been cut up.

The third private railway to introduce Garratts about this time was the metre-gauge Compania Minera de Sierra Menera, which operated a line some 125 miles long for the purpose of conveying

(above) Spain's Rio Tinto Railway hauled 2000 ton trains with metre gauge Garratts, mainly downhill, but on the vacuum brake. No 146 at Los Cañas, in 1961. L. G. Marshall

(below) La Robla Railway Hanomag Garratt No 81 Jose J. de Ampuero, at Valmaseda in 1956. L. G. Marshall

Sierra Menera No 502 heads an ore train from Teruel to Puerto del Escandon, and is banked by an 0—6—6—0 Mallet in 1962. By 1965, the Garratt had *been converted to oil firing, and was in turn the banker. A. E. Durrant*

iron ore from the Ojos Negros mines near Teruel to the Altos Hornos Steelworks on the coast at Sagunto. Generally, the line ran downhill in the loaded direction, and the traffic was hauled by 4—8—0 tender engines. However, from Teruel to Puerto de Escandon, a distance of about 20km, the line climbed from an altitude of approximately 875 to 1200 metres, up which the loaded trains had to be hauled. Contemporary with the 4—8—0s, four 0—6—6—0 Mallets were built for this section and when these required supplementing the Euskalduña Company built two 2—6—2 + 2—6—2 under licence from Beyer Peacock, these again being to the South African Industrial design but altered to suit the metre gauge, and with minor modifications such as the provision of air brakes instead of vacuum.

The operation of this line is interesting, and when the author visited it in 1962, the trains of sturdy four-wheeled hopper wagons were hauled out of Teruel by a Garratt and banked by a Mallet. At Escandon, these handed over to a

4—8—0 and the two articulateds double-headed the empties down to Teruel, giving the rare sight of a Garratt and Mallet double-heading together. By 1965 diesel-hydraulics were virtually monopolising the main stretch from Escandon to Sagunto, but it was interesting to note that steam still performed the hard work, and, with the Mallets falling by the wayside, trains were operated by 4—8—0s banked by a Garratt. Further diesel orders have now been delivered, and the Garratts no longer operate. Building details are:

Engine Nos 501—502 Euskalduna 189—190/ 1930

Main-line Garratts

We now come to the larger Garratts for main-line work in Spain; they were built for the Central of Aragon Railway, which finally extended from Zaragoza and Calatayud, through mountainous Aragon, to Sagunto and Valencia on the

40

The northbound Sevilla to Barcelona express leaves Vinaroz behind a majestic double-Pacific Garratt, in May 1962.   A. E. Durrant

Mediterranean coast. From Teruel to Sagunto the line parallels that of the Sierra Minera, but being of 5ft 6in gauge, the main line, the later of the two to be built, required a separate track which crossed and re-crossed the metre-gauge line at a number of places.

Apart from the iron ore traffic, already handled by the SM, traffic in this region was sparse. Early articulateds were 0—6—6—0T Mallets, later converted to 2—6—6—0 tender engines, and two types of 0—6—6—0 Mallets, the latter built up to 1928. However, the establishment of the railway as a through route to Zaragoza from Valencia brought about an immediate demand for greater power, and two classes of Garratt were supplied in 1931 by Spanish builders under licence from Beyer Peacock.

Pride of the line were the six passenger engines, magnificent 4—6—2 + 2—6—4 with 5ft 9in driving wheels, the largest used on a Garratt at the time. These fine-looking engines were amongst the largest and most powerful passenger types

running in Europe at the time, despite the axle load being limited to 15 tons, and but for the Garratt principle, such power could not have been provided. The designed capacity was the haulage of 300 ton trains at up to 62mph on the level and at 24·5 mph up gradients of 1 in 46 with curves of 300 metres radius.

Mechanically, they included plate frames, piston-valve cylinders with straight ports, and Walschaerts valve gear. The boilers had Belpaire fireboxes and ACFI feed-water heaters, and were, of course, superheated.

The locomotives maintained the passenger service over the line until absorbed into the National system (RENFE) in 1941, when for at least ten years they remained in their original territory, operating from the old Central of Aragon shed at Valencia (Alameda). Eventually, in the 1950s a further duty was found for them, hauling the daily express between Sevilla and Barcelona from Valencia to Tarragona, a route which although not so severe as the C of A, never-

(above) A pair of the original Central Aragon Garratts head out of Fuente Higuera tunnel with fruit bound for northern climes, in 1965. A. E. Durrant

(below) An unusual Garratt duty! Post-war RENFE 282 0422 hauls a broken down ferrobus set between Jativa and La Encina, quite dwarfing the railbus set, in 1965.   A. E. Durrant

theless included gradients of up to 1 in 75. Over this, the train of up to seventeen vehicles with numerous stops required double-heading, and the Garratt was introduced as a successful alternative, running the service until 1966–7, after which diesels took over. As at the end of 1967, despite their age, these locomotives were still considered so useful that they remained in service, working mainly on freight from Valencia to the junction of La Encina, a line of which the 74km from Carcagente to La Encina is solidly uphill with gradients of up to 1 in 75. On their original duties, and later on the Tarragona run, they were the only Garratts regularly used on passenger work in Europe, a duty which they performed with great success for 36 years, which is no mean achievement. No other articulated type has remained in express service for so long and one has been retained for the Spanish railway museum.

For freight traffic, six 2–8–2 + 2–8–2 Garratts were built not, unfortunately, as a freight version of the express engines, but a much smaller conception altogether. Nevertheless, these engines, by Babcock and Wilcox, performed successfully. They possessed generally the features of the larger engines, except that the cylinders had Z ports while the boiler had a round-top firebox. A surprise occurred in 1961 when a further ten of the same basic type were built differing only in minor details from the 1931 batch. These were built new as oil burners, to which by then all the other RENFE Garratts had been converted, and they proved to be the last new steam locomotives built for use in Spain, if not the last in the whole of Europe. The RENFE had, at one time, a project for a large 'super-Garratt', but exactly what this was seems now to be lost.

The 2–8–2 + 2–8–2 Garratts worked, firstly of course, on the C of A and could be found on this route until full dieselisation in 1966–7. They also worked from Valencia to La Encina, and a couple were usually stabled at Játiva where the heavy climbing starts. On this section it was occasionally possible to see double-headed Garratts. Additionally, they worked up the north coast to Tarragona, at which place some were stationed for working the line to Lérida. All are now withdrawn.

Details of building, engines, numbers, etc, for the RENFE Garratts are as below:

C of A Nos	RENFE Nos	Nos/Date
* 101–106	462.0401–06	191–196/1931
† 201–206	282.0401–06	402–407/1931
§ —	282.0421–30	730–739/1960–61
Builder	* Euskalduna	
	† Babcock	
	§ Babcock	

The two Vicineaux 0–6–0 + 0–6–0 tram Garratts rust away in their shed at Lanaeken in July 1953.
L. Rutgers v. Rozenburg

Belgium and Holland

Two surprising applications of the Garratt principle occurred in these countries, on steam tramway systems. Both were introduced at much the same time and each was for a unique type of Garratt, whilst both were of the 0–6–0 + 0–6–0 type.

The two Belgian examples were for the Société National des Chemins de Fer Vicinaux (SNCV), and were metre gauge. They were the only Garratts built as full tram-engines complete with enclosed motion and all-over cab. In appearance they resembled early single-decker motor omnibuses, the front tank representing the bonnet, but underneath was a modern unit of motive power with superheater and piston valves. They were used on the lines Vroenhoven to St Trond and also Tongres-Maaseik hauling loads of sugar-beet, clay, and coal. By 1953 they were derelict in the shed at Lanaeken Tourne-bride, but were doubtless cut up.

The Dutch locomotive was also a tram engine, this time for the N.V. Limburgsche Tramweg Maatschappij, or Limburg tramway, a standard-gauge system upon which it hauled coal trains from Bassenge to Glons. This was a new line, opened in 1922 and closed in 1937, after which the Garratt was stored. During the war it was sent to Germany and put to use, but the author has been unable to discover exact details of where it was used, or its eventual fate.

This little engine was commenced by Hanomag, but completed by Henschel when Hanomag's locomotive business was taken over in 1931. It was unique in being the only Garratt with inside-cylinder units, and was strictly speaking a Union-Garratt, the bunker being on the boiler unit. The

A unique Garratt. Inside cylinders and skirt tanks are typical of Dutch steam tram practice, still to be found in Java, although this Garratt is long since defunct. Author's collection

motion was enclosed in a curious manner, the water tanks being of the pannier type but slung very low down outside the wheels, giving a low centre of gravity but making the motion particularly inaccessible. The superstructure of the engine units comprised only toolboxes and handrails, whilst the boiler unit was conventional, and not enclosed.

These three Low-Countries locomotives were built as below:

Railway	Engine No	Builder and No/Date	
SNCV	850	St Léonard	2121/1929
SNCV	851	St Léonard	2140/1930
Limburg	51	(Hanomag	10758/1931)
		(Henschel	22063/1931)

Russia

The largest Garratt ever built, in terms of weight and overall dimensions, was that which Beyer Peacock produced for the Soviet Railways in 1932. Although exceeded in adhesion weight by the East African 59s, and equalled in tractive effort by South Africa's GL, the Russian Я—01 can safely be claimed the largest Garratt built, the boiler being of unexcelled dimensions.

Extremely sound and simple in design, the Garratt was of the 4—8—2 + 2—8—4 type, with bar frames, modern straight-ported cylinders, and drive through long connecting rods onto the third coupled axle of each unit. The boiler had a round-top firebox fired by a mechanical stoker and, due to the expected ambient temperatures, dropping to minus 30°C, all steam pipes were made to drain, so that when the locomotive was standing there would be no water to freeze up.

Its immense size is not obvious in illustrations, as Russia's 17ft 0in loading gauge allowed tall chimney and domes to be mounted on the boiler which belied its massive bulk. Designed to haul 2500 ton trains, and to have an axle load not exceeding 20 tons, the Я—01 can be considered a competitor to Russia'a own 4—14—4. No trouble should have been expected, following Russia's extensive experience with the Fairlie and Mallet articulated locomotives, but somehow it did not come up to expectations and is reported to have been dismantled in 1937.

On test in the Sverdlovsk area, mainly from Chelyabinsk, in the Southern Urals, temperatures of minus 41°C were encountered, probably the coldest in which a Garratt ever operated, as they were generally warm-country engines. The Russians never took to the Garratt and settled for reduced train loads, within the capacity of a 2—10—2. When, many years later, they decided that this was insufficient, just before the end of

EUROPE

Class	Type	Cylinders Dia × Stroke (in)	Coupled Wheel Dia (ft in)	Boiler Press (psi)	Tractive Effort @ 75% (lb)	Grate Area (sq ft)	Max Boiler Dia (ft in)	Heating Surface (sq ft) Fire-box	Tubes	Super-heater	Weights in Working Order (Tons) Max Axle	Ad-hesive	Total	Wtr (Gal)	Fuel (Tons /Gal)	Literature Reference	Remarks
London & North Eastern Railway																	
U1	2-8-0 + 0-8-2	(6)18½×26	4-8	180	64350	56·5	Outs 7-0	224	2644	650	18·3	144	178	5000	7t	L204/25	
London Midland & Scottish Railway																	
	2-6-0 + 0-6-2	18½×26	5-3	190	40250	44·5	6-9	183	1954	500	20·25 21·0 20·3	116·5 121·5 119·45	148·75 155·5 152·8	4500 4500 4500	7t 9t 9t	L176/27 L330/30	Locos 4997-9 As Built Locos with Rotating Bunker Locos 4967-96 As Built
Industrial Locomotives in Britain																	
	0-4-0 + 0-4-0	13½×20* 14×20	3-4	180* 185	24600* 27200	22·7	5-0	107	1299	Nil	16·5	61·5	61·5	1500+ 1380	1·5t	L106/32 L74/24 IRR252/66	Sneyd Collieries* Vivians GKN, Atherstone †Vivians only
Central of Aragon/RENFE																	
462 0401	4-6-2 + 2-6-4	19×26	5-9	200	40880	53·0	6-7⅜	275	2943	742	15·75	92·35	180·5	4840	7·5t	L188/31	
282 0401	2-8-2 + 2-8-2	17·3×24	3-11¼	213	49000	45·2	6-4	171	1947	737	13·5	108·0	161·5	4840	9t	L58/32	
282 0421	2-8-2 + 2-8-2	17·3×24	3-11¼	213	49000	45·2	6-4	169	1952	747	14·55	114·13	170·25	5610	13·5t		
La Robla																	
	2-6-2 + 2-6-2	16·6×21·7	3-6¼	185	39000	34·5	5-7	129	1420	388	12·6	73·18	108·03	3300	8t		
FF CC Catalanes																	
	2-6-2 + 2-6-2	14·18×19·4	3-3⅜	171	25700	29·6	—	114·5	1330	291	10·8	64·65	78·2	1431	3·5t		
Sierra Menera																	
	2-6-2 + 2-6-2	17×22	3-6¾	180	40150	41·9	6-1½	171·5	1835·5	448	14·2	83·45	118·15	3520	6·9t	L189/31	
Rio Tinto																	
	2-6-2 + 2-6-2	17×22	3-6¾	200	44610	41·7	6-1½	171	1831	448	13·5	81·0	119·0	4000	7t	G975/35	
Holland—Limburg Tram																	
	0-6-0 + 0-6-0	14·2×14·2	2-11·4	198	23150	21·5	—	933		450	12	71·5	71·5	1540	3t	H27/32	
Belgium—SNCV																	
	0-6-0 + 0-6-0	14·2×13·8	2-11·4	198	22500	21·6	—	896		218	10	60	60			Q46/30 L300/30	
USSR																	
Я	4-8-2 + 2-8-4	22·43×28	4-11	220	78700	85·5	7-6	343	3227	970	19·75	156	262·5	8110	16t	RE3/33 L4/33	

*The largest Garratt ever built, USSR's solitary Я-01,
which saw but short service.* Beyer Peacock

steam development, a return was made to the simple-expansion Mallet for their prototype locomotives.

Я—01 was Beyer Peacock's works number 6737, dated 1932.

Miniature Locomotives

Whilst model locomotives are not within the scope of this book, it is worth mentioning the miniature Garratts built for the Surrey Border & Camberley Railway, a 10¼in-gauge pleasure line which nevertheless carried passengers for revenue.

In 1938, Kitsons supplied two 2—6—0 + 0—6—2 Garratts for this line, supposedly based upon the LMS examples, but bearing little resemblance to

*Built as a miniature railway Garratt, for the SB&CR,
10¼in gauge* Jason *is seen as rebuilt to more
orthodox 'narrow gauge' form.* B. Roberts

them. They were numbered 4012 and 4013 and put in very little work, as due to the war, the railway, being inessential and also inaccessible otherwise than by motor car, was closed. No 4013 was sold to the Maharaja of Baroda and shipped to India, while 4012, after passing through various ownerships, was later on the railway serving Sir Thomas Salt's pig farm at Shillingstone, Dorset. This engine had been altered by the addition of a tall chimney, dome, and cab so that it now resembles a bona fide narrow-gauge Garratt. It bears the number 4, and name *Jason*, but having scale-size tyres and flanges was prone to derailment and therefore was seldom used to haul pig food. By 1980, following disposal of the Shillingstone line, No 4012 was in private ownership at Wimborne, Dorset, while No 4013 was in a private collection in Norfolk. Two new miniature Garratts built in the 1970s just qualify for mention here as although built for 7¼in gauge they are passenger haulers of high capacity and capable of hard commercial work. Both are approximately 1:5 scale models of EAR's 59 class locomotives, designed by Neil Simkins, one built by Coleby-Simkins of Leicestershire, the other by Milner Engineering of Chester. Both are oil fired. They can haul about 150 passengers on the level. One is on a private railway in North Wales with gradients of 1 in 22 and curves of 50ft radius on a mountainside — ideal Garratt country!

Chapter 4

Asia

Asia, with its general lack of heavy industry, was not a continent where freight trains of maximum capacity could be extensively employed. As a result, eight-coupled tender engines were generally adequate for freight traffic, and only rarely was it necessary to exceed their powers of haulage. Hence, there were comparatively few Garratts, and the bulk of these were divided between India and Burma.

India

The term India, for the purpose of this book, includes the railways of the old British India, as it was during the period of British rule that all the Garratts used on the subcontinent were supplied. While some were at one time used in areas now included in Pakistan, that country no longer possesses any form of articulated steam power.

The first true Garratt — Darjeeling Himalaya Railway. Note the extraordinary reversing gear, with crude expansion and universal joints; clearly Beyer

Actually, India was the second country to introduce the Garratt type, and in fact the first true Garratt, that is with simple-expansion cylinders at the outer ends of the power bogies, was for this country.

Darjeeling-Himalaya Railway

This little line, of 2ft gauge, is one of the world's most difficult to operate. Connecting with the metre gauge at Siliguri, the line climbs fifty-one miles into the mountains to Darjeeling, for much of the way on 1 in 30 gradients, and over curves as sharp as 90ft radius. Even these severe conditions are inadequate to gain altitude sufficiently without additional devices such as complete loops in some places, and zig-zag reversing stations at others. The maximum altitude reached is 7407ft.

Peacock were still learning when they built this one! Note also the re-railing pole slung alongside the boiler frame. W. H. C. Kelland

*North Western Railway of India; class GA Garratt
No 480.* Beyer Peacock

Most of the work on the line had always been done with 0—4—0T locomotives of various types, but it was in 1910 that Beyer Peacock produced for this little line their second design of Garratt, this being the first true Garratt. It was of the 0—4—0 + 0—4—0 type, with the general dimensions predictably equal to two of the larger 0—4—0T engines.

Outside frames were used, and the slide-valve cylinders had steam distribution by Walschaerts gear. The Belpaire boiler was not superheated and, an unusual feature, infrequently repeated, was the well tank slung under the boiler barrel. The cab was completely open on both sides, being simply a roof supported on columns but with spectacle plates fore and aft.

For some reason, the engine was not considered a success, and although not withdrawn from service until 1954, was used but infrequently. No doubt the possession of one engine of double the normal power presented operating difficulties in finding adequate train loads, while possibly the maximum loads were greater than the sidings, or couplers, could accommodate. Equally, such an embryonic Garratt probably contained a number of details which had yet to be perfected, and which may have given trouble. Nevertheless, the engine lasted forty-four years, which is not to be sneezed at.

Building details are: Beyer Peacock No 5407 of 1910, Darjeeling Himalaya Rly Class 'D', engine No 31.

North Western Railway

The NWR was India's largest railway system, comprising about 6600 route miles of track, divided now between the Pakistan Railways and the Northern Railway of India. In the furthest north section, now in Pakistan, were some extremely difficult sections including the Quetta line where, through the Bolan pass, gradients of 1 in 25 had to be surmounted. Normal power units on this division were the HGS 2—8—0, and up to four were required on a heavy train. Naturally, this was hardly an economical method of working and in about 1923 a Baldwin-built compound 2—6—6—2 was placed in service, the general idea being to replace two 2—8—0s. Then, in 1925, Beyer Peacock built a 2—6—2 + 2—6—2 Garratt to test not only against the Mallet but also against a pair of 2—8—0s.

According to Beyer Peacock's catalogue, the Garratt was able to manage 354 tons compared with 160 tons for a 2—8—0. The principal dimensions of the Garratt were obviously arranged to afford a direct comparison with the Mallet rather than with a pair of Consolidations, with the idea of determining which type of articulated to adopt in India, when loads were too great for conventional types.

Beyer Peacock, of course, claimed that their Garratt was an immense success, but clearly, when weather conditions become difficult, it is impossible to replace eight-coupled units with

The Bengal Nagpur class N Garratt in first and final form, with piston valves. Indian Railways 38818 leaves Kusumkasa loop in 1970, with a 2400 tonne ore train bound for Bhilai steelworks. A. E. Durrant

six-coupled. As a result, neither the Garratt nor the Mallet was considered a complete success on the NWR and they were not repeated. In later years they were transferred to the more easily graded Rawalpindi section where the ruling gradient is only 1 in 100 and where they could take a double load.

No doubt a larger, eight-coupled Garratt as supplied to the BNR would have proved more effective and might well have been purchased, but for the fact that the Great Indian Peninsular Railway, having electrified its 'Ghat' or mountain sections, had surplus some thirty large four-cylinder 2—10—0s of Class 'N', which had a haulage capacity approximately equal to that of the Garratt and Mallet. Doubtless purchased at a bargain price, these remained the heavy freight power on the NWR until replaced by diesels.

The Garratt and the Mallet, being non-standard, were scrapped after a fairly short life, the Garratt in 1937.

Details of this NWR Garratt were quite sound and straightforward; it had two cylinder units with plate frames, and modern, straight-ported cylinders, the drive being to the third axle of each unit. The boiler was superheated, with a Belpaire firebox, and conformed generally to Indian standards. There seems no doubt that the design, which otherwise appeared very sound indeed, was simply too small for the job, and was probably deliberately so in order to effect a direct comparison with the Mallet. It is of interest to compare the principal dimensions and capacities of the four competing types and these are tabulated below.

The NWR Garratt was railway No 480, Class GAS, and built by Beyer Peacock, No 6203, in 1925.

The Bengal Nagpur Railway

Whilst the NWR were playing with a six-coupled

Class	HGS	Mallet	N	Garratt
Type	2-8-0	2-6-6-2	2-10-0	2-6-2 + 2-6-2
Cylinders	(2) 22in × 26in	(4) 19in/29½in × 30in	(4) 20in × 26in	(4) 18½in × 26in
Coupled wheels	4ft 8½in	4ft 4in	4ft 8½in	4ft 3in
Tractive effort (lb)	60136*	46400	49700	47110
Grate area (sq ft)	64*	56·25	45	56·5
Adhesion weight (tons)	128·5*	104·8	94·3	115·4
Total weight (tons)	274*	187·7	174·4	178·4

*Combined figures for two locomotives. All tractive efforts at 75 per cent boiler pressure

49

A remarkable collection of men, including army officer, lined up beside BNR class N Garratt No 825, fitted with Caprotti poppet valves. W. H. C. Kelland

Garratt, the BNR, who operated a heavy coal traffic with 1,600 ton trains, were also trying out the type, again to eliminate the double-heading of the old standard 2—8—0s. In this case the sensible course was adopted of making the Garratt the equal of two 2—8—0s, the whole of the motion being standard. Upon this was mounted a large Belpaire boiler, with rather more than double the grate area of a 2—8—0. This was, of course, superheated and despite its size, hand fired. The frames were of plate, in accordance with British-Indian practice of the time, and the two locomotives were put to work on the Chakardarpur-Jharsuguda section, where they effectively managed the double 2—8—0 loads. This section is now electrified, and the two engines once out of use at Kharagpur are doubtless scrapped.

The success of these two engines led to the ordering of a further sixteen Garratts, built in 1929, these being substantially larger. The 4—8—0 + 0—8—4 wheel arrangement was used (it is not found on any railway apart from the BNR), and with a permissible axle load of just over 20 tons, the opportunity was taken of substantially increasing the tractive effort, and also the water capacity, which latter figure is the greatest of any Garratt. The original boiler on the 2—8—0 +

0—8—2 had proved perfectly adequate, and was only slightly enlarged on the new design.

Cylinder design was looked at thoroughly, and of this 'N' class, Nos 810—819 had modern straightported piston-valve cylinders of considerably superior design to those of the old BESA 2—8—0s and corresponding HSG Garratt, although whether superior design showed up to much advantage in slow, heavy haulage is a moot point. Nos 820—22 had RC type poppet valves for comparison. while Nos 823—25 used Caprotti gear. All six poppet valve engines later had piston valves and Walschaerts gear.

These were the largest locomotives ever to run in India, a record which still stands today. Originally used on coal traffic between Chakardhapore and Jharsuguda, Anara to Tatanagar, and also to Asansol, they were last used in 1970—71 hauling 2400 ton iron ore trains from Dalli Rajhara to Bhilai.

With their heavy axle load, the 'N' class were restricted to the main lines and branches laid with 90lb rail, but their ability to haul up to 2400 tons up a 1 in 100 gradient, and to reach maximum speeds of 45mph, set a standard of performance which could be well appreciated on certain more lightly laid branches.

50

(above) Climbing into the Shan mountains, Burma Railways class GB No 822 has attained an altitude of 3,924ft (1,196m), at a reversing station in Gurkha country. R. A. Kingsford-Smith

(below) A 1700 ton ore train from Broken Hill to Port Pirie is seen here behind South Australian 3ft 6in gauge Garratt No 402, preparing to leave Gladstone in 1969. R. A. Kingsford-Smith

(above)　A southbound freight battles up the 1 in 75 to Hawkmount summit, hauled by one of Australia's most powerful steam locomotives, NSWGR class AD60 4—8—4 + 4—8—4 Garratt.　R. A. Kingsford Smith

(below) East Africa　In Mombasa shed, a diminutive class 24 4—8—0 is intimidated by gigantic class 59 Garratts, still largely very clean during the last few years of steam operation.　A. E. Durrant

BNR class N at work, as fitted with rotary cam poppet valves. These were later replaced by piston valve cylinders. W. H. C. Kelland

Accordingly, in 1931, a further ten Garratts of a modified design, Class 'NM', were supplied, these differing from Class 'N' in having Lentz poppet valves and greatly reduced fuel and water capacities, so that the axle load could be reduced to 17 tons. There was an excess of weight in the original 'N' design, and only a token reduction of tractive effort was made. The firebox, however, was fitted with thermic syphons and arch tubes as an aid to even better performance. The class was stationed at Sahdol for working the line from Bilaspur to Katni, and also on the Anuppur-Chirmiri branch, serving the coalfields in the area. Although later than the N class, the NM, probably due to their poppet valves, were withdrawn by the late 1960s.

On this latter branch, with its severe curvature, it was found desirable to have Garratts with carrying wheels at the inner ends of the power units, and accordingly, in 1939, the final BNR class, 'P', was produced. These 4—8—2 + 2—8—4s were direct derivations of the 'N' and 'NM' classes, having the piston-valve cylinders of the earlier 'Ns' plus a slightly enlarged thermic syphon boiler of the 'NM' type. Coal and water capacities were increased from the 'NM' values, but not to the extent of the 'Ns', while with the

extra two pairs of wheels, the axle loading remained as on the 'NMs', making the locomotives suitable for 75lb track. Loads of 1500 tons are normally hauled on this branch up gradients of 1 in 91, while up to 1750 tons have been hauled on occasions. The P class also finished their days at Bhilai, lasting to about 1971. Both N and P classes have a member preserved for the Indian Railways museum at New Delhi.

Building data for all the BNR Garratts, which later ran on the Indian State South Eastern Railway, are tabulated below:

Class	BNR Nos	ISR (SER) Nos	B.P. Nos	Date
HSG	691—2	38691—2	6261—2	1925
N	810—25	38810—25	6583—98	1929
NM	826—35	38826—35	6705—14	1931
P	855—58	38855—58	6931—34	1939

The Assam Bengal Railway

This railway, which was situated in the far north-east corner of India, is in rugged country bordering Burma, China, and what is now

53

BNR class NM, with Lentz poppet valves, at Bhojudih Junction shed. These retained poppet valves, and were withdrawn before the older class N. W. H. C. Kelland

Bangladesh. From near the Bangladesh border, at Badarpur, to a junction at Lumding, is a metre-gauge line through the hills, with a ruling gradient of 1 in 37 between Jatinga and Harangajao for which, in 1927, the ABR purchased five 2—6—2 + 2—6—2 Garratts.

These were of modest capacity although, due to the unrestricted Indian metre-gauge clearances, of massive appearance, and were simple plate-framed jobs, with modern piston-valve cylinders, and a superheated Belpaire boiler. The introduction of these engines enabled loads to be increased from 230 tons for the standard 4—8—0 to 300 tons for the Garratt, assistance being provided for both types over the steepest section.

In 1942, the railway switched its name around, becoming the Bengal Assam Railway, and during the Burma Campaign, a number of the War Department Garratts were allocated to the BAR. Full details of these will be found in Chapter 11, on Wartime Garratts, and nine of them remained behind after the war, these being of the 4—8—2 + 2—8—4 type.

At the partition of India and Pakistan, the railway became the Assam Railway for a while, and is now the North East Frontier Railway of India. The original ABR 2—6—2 + 2—6—2,

reduced to four by the cannibalisation of two engines after a collision, together with the nine ex-WD locomotives, were joined by four new 4—8—2 + 2—8—4s originally built for Burma, but soon sold to the NEFR. The data below set out details of these engines as running on the NEFR, together with their various renumberings etc.

ABR Class T	Nos 401—5, Beyer Peacock 6385—89 of 1927.
	Became BAR Class 'GT', Nos 191—95 in 1942.
	191, withdrawn, parts going into No 194.
	Renumbered 671—74, thence to Assam Rly.
	Became NER Nos 971—74.
	Finally NEFR Nos 32078—81.
BAR Class MWGX	(Ex-WD) see Chapter 11. Nine locomotives became NER 975—83.
	Finally NEFR 32082—90.
Ex-Burma locomotives	Four locomotives ex BR. Became NER Nos 984—87.
	Finally NEFR 32091—94.

(above) Largest of the BNR Garratts were the class
P, one of which is seen basking in its own reflection
at Bhilai during the 1970 monsoons.   A. E. Durrant

(below) Metre gauge Assam Bengal Garratt No 401
ready for action on the hill section.
W. H. C. Kelland

Burma

Burma Railways

The Burma Railways possess an extremely severe hill section, on the Lashio branch where, between Sedaw and Thondaung, a distance of eleven miles, there is a ruling gradient of 1 in 25 which, being uncompensated for reverse curves of 350ft radius, is equal to a 1 in 21·4 gradient.

The first articulated locomotives delivered for this duty were eight Vulcan Foundry 0—6—6—0T Fairlies, built in 1906, and these were followed after the First World War by five batches of the standard North British 0—6—6—0 Mallet tender locomotives. All the above locomotives were limited by the 10 ton axle load to 60 tons adhesion weight. The Fairlies had rather more tractive effort, but the Mallets the larger boiler, later superheated, so that the haulage capacity of the two was about equal, the Mallets being handicapped by having to lug 36 tons of tender upgrade.

By the time that traffic had increased sufficiently to require eight-coupled articulateds, the Garratt had appeared on the scene, and an experimental 2—8—0 + 0—8—2 was supplied in 1924, this, incidentally, being the first eight-coupled Garratt ever built.

The design was typical of contemporary Garratt practice, a superheated Belpaire boiler feeding the cylinders, which were straight ported and mounted on plate frames. The tanks were, of course, of the all square corner type. Within the same overall weight as the Mallet plus its tender, the Garratt was able to include about one-third more tractive effort, adhesion weight, and boiler capacity, at the expense of a reduction in coal capacity. In service the Garratt could haul 210 tons compared with the Mallet's 145 tons, which was rather better than the nominal differences between the two classes, whilst the Garratt also showed a fuel economy of 18·5 per cent.

Following the success of this engine, a further four Garratts of similar power were ordered, and built in 1927. In general, the principal variations consisted of increasing the cab length, raising the bunker and tanks to a higher level well clear of the motion, and rounding the top sides of the front tanks. The last three engines retained the same nominal dimensions as the first Garratt, but the first engine of this batch differed in being a compound, the second and last design of compound Garratt actually built.

As in the original Tasmanian compound Garratt, the high-pressure cylinders were on the rear, and the low-pressure on the front unit, but all were positioned as on normal Garratts, at the outer ends of the engine units. The compound, due to the weight of its large low-pressure

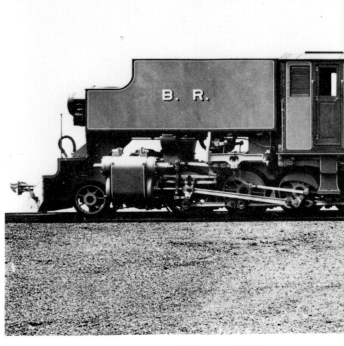

The second, and last, compound Garratt design actually built was this 2—8—0 + 0—8—2 for Burma Railways. Low pressure cylinders are on the front engine unit. Beyer Peacock

cylinders, was somewhat heavier than either of the simple types, despite having reduced coal and water capacities. In service, it showed no advantage over the simple-expansion type, and in further orders, compounding was abandoned.

In the next order, for eight Garratts, it was decided to increase the coal capacity by about one ton, and this was achieved by rearranging the proportions of both front and rear tank capacities, in order to distribute the additional weight evenly. Messrs Krupp of Essen won the order for these engines, much to the annoyance of Beyer Peacock. The chairman, Sir Sam Fay, commenting on these and the SAR German-built Garratts, at the Beyer Peacock annual general meeting in 1931, said that whereas British tenderers for equipment to Colonial markets had to state whether or not they were on the King's Roll for employment of men disabled in the 1914—18 war, contracts were being awarded to the country which caused those disablements. Whether or not the warnings were really heeded is unknown as the subsequent slump cut down locomotive purchases throughout the world, but the fact remains that German builders supplied no further Garratts to British possessions, although they continued to compete successfully for conventional locomotives.

By the end of the slump, when further Garratts

The original Burma Railways class GA Garratt poses for the official photographer at a reversing station on the 1 in 25 Hill section. Beyer Peacock

were being considered, it had been decided that to reduce flange wear, a 2–8–2 + 2–8–2 type should be adopted, but before this could be implemented, a further war was in progress.

For the Far East theatre, where metre gauge prevailed, there arose, in 1943, an urgent need for metre-gauge Garratts, and the Burma Railway 2–8–0 + 0–8–2 was chosen as the basis, the third series with its lower coal capacity being decided upon, largely no doubt because this was the last series produced by Beyer Peacock. The previous Garratts, of all four variations were all classed GA, differentiated into batches I, II, III, and IV, and while the next ten engines strictly come into Chapter 11, they eventually became Class GB.

While the GBs were being produced, the necessary design modifications to give the intended 2–8–2 + 2–8–2 type were put in hand, these being next built, and were eventually to become BR Class GC.

A far larger 4–8–2 + 2–8–4 was also put in hand with larger wheels and coal and water capacities, those of this type that remained in Burma becoming Class GD.

Finally, in 1949, a modified GD class, with 'streamlined' tanks, was built for Burma, but due to the political upheavals in the country at the time, six of these went straight to East Africa, and the remaining four ended up on the Indian North Eastern Railway, having done little work in Burma. The reason, of course, for these Garratts being surplus was that terrorist activities had prevented the reopening of certain lines upon which these Garratts should have worked.

By 1946, all the batches of Class GA were out of service due to wartime damage, while a report in 1955 showed that all the GB, GC, and GD Garratts were in service. Burma has been slowly dieselising for many years, but diesel unreliability has led to the retention of many steam engines, including several Garratts. However, they are no longer used on the mountain lines, but perform odd duties such as ballast workings along the level sections. Indeed, one report recently indicated that a Garratt was operating with the front unit totally inoperative, becoming in the process a 10–8–2 wheel arrangement!

The extremely dinky Garratt designed and built for the defunct Buthidaung-Maungdaw tramway in Burma. Beyer Peacock

Buthidaung-Maungdan Tramway

This little tramway, of 2ft 6in gauge, was owned by the Arakan Flotilla Company, and commenced operations with two little Garratts, 0–6–0 + 0–6–0 built by Beyer Peacock in 1913. These outside-framed jobs, which were not superheated, rank as the second smallest Garratts built, being but half a ton heavier than those for the Congo Mayumbe Railway, whilst the axle load of 4 tons was among the lightest used. The tramway itself

BURMA RAILWAYS—BUILDING DATA

Class	Type	Engine Nos	Builder	Builders' Nos	Date
GA I	2-8-0 + 0-8-2	21	BP	6180	1924
GA II	,,	208	,,	6354	1927
GA III	,,	209-11	,,	6411-13	,,
GA IV	,,	485-92	Krupp	1077-84	1929
GB	,,	821-30	BP	(See Chapter 11)	1943
GC	2-8-2 + 2-8-2	831-42	,,	,,	,,
GD	4-8-2 + 2-8-4	851-4/65-9	,,	,,	,,
GE	,,	861-4	,,	7286-89	1949

(below) Towards the end of its life, a Burma Railways
class GC stands at Thazi Junction shed in 1972.
R. A. Kingsford-Smith

*The prototype class C1 Garratt on the Ceylon
Government Railways, later multiplied as class C1A,
which later survived to see the country called Sri
Lanka.* W. H. C. Kelland

had but a short life, closing in 1926, and the two Garratts presumably lay derelict until they rusted to pieces. The building data are:

No 1 *Buthidaung* Beyer Peacock 5702/1913
,, 2 *Maungdan* ,, 5703 ,,

Sri Lanka (formerly Ceylon)

The railways of Sri Lanka are, surprisingly, built mainly to 5ft 6in gauge, although the locomotives used on them have generally been of about the size associated with the metre gauge in neighbouring India. The normal locomotives used were 4—6—0s, and some 4—8—0s were built for the hill sections, the general axle load limit being 10 tons.

In 1927, an experimental 2—6—2 + 2—6—2 Garratt was placed in service on the Rambukkana to Kadugannawa section, thirteen miles long, at the foothills of the Kandyan mountains, the ruling gradient being 1 in 45.

The engine had plate frames, modern piston-valve cylinders and a superheated Belpaire boiler, and in service successfully hauled the 283 ton train normally worked by two 4—6—0 tender engines, and in doing so saved 20·5 per cent coal, 15·5 per cent water, and of course one engine crew.

As this engine, like the heavy 4—8—0s with 15 ton axle load, was restricted to a limited route mileage, no further examples were built until

1946, when eighteen were supplied by Beyer Peacock, the track having by then been improved to take them. They were modified in a number of ways, chief being the inclusion of thermic syphons and also Hadfield power reversers. Despite the steady dieselisation in Sri Lanka, the post war Garratts held on to several duties on the mountainous line to Kandy, the last few not being withdrawn until the late 1970s.

Ceylon also had a tiny 2—4—0 + 0—4—2 Garratt for its 2ft 6in gauge branch up the Kelani Valley line from Colombo to Opanake, which has a ruling gradient of 1 in 24. This little engine was designed to replace two of the 0—4—2Ts which previously worked the line; it was an outside-framed job with, of course, plate frames. The piston-valve cylinders were fed with superheated steam from the Belpaire boiler and, like the broad-gauge engines, the tank sides had rounded tops. The Garratts built for Ceylon were as below:

		Engine	B-Peacock	
Gauge	Class	Nos	Nos	Date
5ft 6in	C1	241	6410	1927
,,	C1A	343-50	7160-67	1945
2ft 6in	H1	293	6629	1929

*Ceylon's unique narrow gauge class H1 2—4—0 +
0—4—2 Garratt.*   Beyer Peacock

Nepal Government Railways Garratt No 6 Sitarama
at Simra in April 1958.   Derek Cross

Nepal

High up in the Himalayas, the Nepal Government Railway naturally has some severe climbing
to do with its 2ft 6in-gauge railway, and in 1932 a
Garratt was purchased, of similar design to that
built for the Sierra Leone Government Railways
in West Africa.

The line runs from Birgenj (in India) to Simra,
after which very steep gradients, up to 1 in 30, are
encountered to the terminus at Amlekhganj, from
where a road and a ropeway make connection to
Katmandu.

In 1947 a further Garratt was built, and just
before Beyer Peacock closed down the NGR put
out an enquiry for a third engine which, unfortunately, was never ordered.

The main duty of these Garratts was in hauling
the daily freight over the length of the line, but on
the occasion of the monthly fair at Amlekhganj,
the Garratt piloted the 0—6—2T of the
strengthened passenger train, now discontinued,

Royal Siamese State Railway Garratt No 454 at Bangkok in 1952. One of these Henschel built locomotives is preserved. A. Elyard Brown

over the steep stretch from Simra. The two engines built were:

No 4	Mahabir	Beyer Peacock	6736/1932
„ 6	Sitarama	„	7243/1947

Thailand (formerly Siam)

For working the heaviest sections of the Royal State Railways of Siam, Messrs Henschel in 1929 supplied six 2—8—2 + 2—8—2 wood-burning Garratts which were the most powerful steam locomotives to run in Siam. Designed to haul 530 ton trains up gradients as steep as 1 in 42, these engines had bar frames, but cylinders with Z ports for the piston-valves. The round-top boiler was, of course, superheated, and contained nothing in the way of arch tubes or thermic syphons. Following the success of the first six, a further two were supplied in 1936.

After the war a dieselisation policy was instituted, and among the victims were the Garratts, which were withdrawn between 1950 and 1964. Happily, No 457, the last in service, is among a number of steam engines saved for preservation, and is currently in Bangkok works. Construction details are:

RSR	451-6	Henschel	21618-23/1929
„	457-8	„	23109-10/1936

ASIA MINOR

Turkey

Only one Garratt was built for use in Turkey, predictably by Beyer Peacock for the British-owned Ottoman Railway Company which ran from Smyrna (Izmir) to Aidin, and was finally extended to Egridir. From Selçuk to Çamlik the line climbed through the Azizieh Pass, with gradients as steep as 1 in 36, and it was for helper duties on this section that the Garratt was acquired. This plate-framed, Belpaire-boilered job was from the outset hamstrung by the

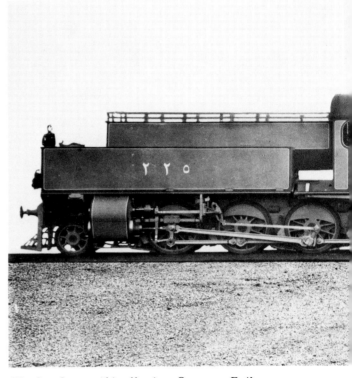

The handsome, if ineffective, Ottoman Railway unsuperheated 2—8—0 + 0—8—2, Turkey's only Garratt. Beyer Peacock

conservative policies of the ORC, and used flat slide valves to distribute the unsuperheated steam, which was quite ridiculous for a 2—8—0 + 0—8—2, of standard gauge, built in 1927. In fact, it was not until two years later than the ORC took delivery of their first superheated locomotive. On 1 June 1935 the ORC was absorbed into the Turkish State Railway (TCDD) system, and soon after the Garratt seems to have disappeared, there being no evidence that it ever received a TCDD number.

ORC No 225 was built by Beyer Peacock, No 6324, in 1927.

Iran

The other railway in Asia Minor to use Garratts was the Iranian State Railways, which took delivery of four 4—8—2 + 2—8—4s for use on the northern section of their main line, which crosses the Elburz mountains, climbing to an altitude of nearly 7000ft, with gradients of up to 1 in 36 continuously for forty miles on the northern ascent. Loads of 400 tons could be handled over this section in good weather, but with the usual icy conditions, 350 tons was the normal load.

The engines were of modern design, although with plate frames, and had straight-ported

A wartime photograph of an Iranian Garratt on the northern section of the Trans-Persian State Railway, at Sorkhabal station. Author's collection

piston-valve cylinders. The boiler was super-heated, and the round-top firebox, which burned oil, contained arch tubes.

The four locomotives built by Beyer Peacock, works Nos 6787—90 dated 1936, were at first numbered 418—21, later becoming 86.01—04, '8' denoting the number of coupled, and '6' the number of carrying axles. Although the line had been fully dieselised for a number of years, most of the steam fleet remained in reserve, including the Garratts which were noted at Teheran in December 1966.

INDO-CHINA

The metre-gauge railways of Indo-China had six Garratts, numbered 201—206, purchased second-hand from the Kenya Uganda Railway in 1939. Full details of these will be found in Chapter 10, but no information is to hand as to their subsequent fate in this war-torn part of the world, now known as Vietnam.

ASIA

Class	Type	Cylinders Dia × Stroke (in)	Coupled Wheel Dia (ft in)	Boiler Press (psi)	Tractive Effort @ 75% (lb)	Grate Area sq ft	Max Boiler Dia (Outs) ft in	Heating Surface (sq ft) Fire-box	Heating Surface (sq ft) Tubes	Heating Surface (sq ft) Super-heater	Weights in Working Order (Tons) Max Axle	Weights in Working Order (Tons) Ad-hesive	Weights in Working Order (Tons) Total	Wtr Cpcty (Gal)	Fuel Cpcty (Tons /Gal)	Literature Reference	Remarks
Darjeeling Himalaya Railway																W181	
D	0-4-0 + 0-4-0	11×14	2-2	160	13530	17·5	3-10⅞	64	603	Nil	7·4	28·0	28·0	600	1t	L85/11	
North Western Railway																W205	
GAS	2-6-2 + 2-6-2	18½×26	4-3	180	47110	56·5	6-10	235	2469	550	19·5	115·4	178·4	6500	11t	L269/25	
																RE399/25	
Bengal Nagpur Railway																L46/26	
HSG	2-8-0 + 0-8-2	20×26	4-8	180	50140	67·3	7-1 9/16	263	2954	642	18·75	148·5	180·5	5000	8t	L104/25	
																RE95/30	
N	4-8-0 + 0-8-4	20½×26	4-8	210	61460	69·8	7-1 13/16	286	3118	642	20·25	159·4	234·0	10000	14t	L113/30	
NM	4-8-0 + 0-8-4	20×26	4-8	210	58500	67·6	7-1 13/16	330	2961	642	17·15	138·55	204·15	6000	8t	L256/31	
																G15/40	
P	4-8-2 + 2-8-4	20½×26	4-8	210	61460	70·0	7-1 13/16	333	3120	661	17·0	136·0	230·0	7500	10t	L117/40	
Assam Bengal Railway																	
T	2-6-2 + 2-6-2	14×24	4-0	180	26460	30·0	5-4½	132	1298	268	9·5	57·0	90·2	2400	6t	L6/28	
Burma Railways																	
GA I	2-8-0 + 0-8-2	15½×20	3-3	180	33260	43·9	5-7⅜	183·5	1551·5	365	10·1	80·3	99·1	2000	4t	L366/23	
																G562/27	
GA II	2-8-0 + 0-8-2	17½/26½×20	3-3	200	34550	43·9	5-7⅜	183·5	1551·5	319	10·65	84·4	103·4	1780	4t	L4/28	
GA III	2-8-0 + 0-8-2	15½×20	3-3	180	33260	43·9	5-7⅜	183·5	1551·5	319	10·5	83·8	101·6	2000	5t		
GA IV	2-8-0 + 0-8-2	15½×20	3-3	200	36960	43·9	5-7⅜	183·5	1551·5	409	10·9	84·55	104·55	2000	6·2t		
GB	2-8-0 + 0-8-2	15½×20	3-3	200	36960	43·7	5-7⅜	187·0	1555	313	10·5	83·75	103·35	2000	5t	G187/44	
																G187/44	
GC	2-8-2 + 2-8-2	15½×20	3-3	200	36960	43·7	5-8⅞	187·0	1555	313	10·5	83·45	117·85	3600	6t	L100/48	
GD	4-8-2 + 2-8-4	16×24	4-0	200	38400	48·75	6-0	183·0	1813	399	10·0	80·0	136·8	4200	7t		
GE	4-8-2 + 2-8-4		See East African 56 class														
Buthidaung Maungdan Tramway																	
	0-6-0 + 0-6-0	8½×12	2-0	180	9754	12	3-8	50	472	Nil	3·95	23·55	23·55	550	¾t		
Ceylon																	
CI	2-6-2 + 2-6-2	16×22	3-7	180	35360	44·8	6-0	174	1652	346	13·4	79·8	122·9	4000	7t		
CIA	2-6-2 + 2-6-2	16×22	3-7	185	36350	44·9	6-0	220	1640	362	13·5	80·9	128·8	4000	7t	G394/45	
HI	2-4-0 + 0-4-2	10×16	2-6	175	14000	14·9	3-10	58	434	82	7·0	28·0	39·0	1000	2t	L221/30	
Nepal																	
	2-6-2 + 2-6-2	10×16	2-4	175	15000	18·2		76·5	647·5	120	5·0	30·3	47·5	1300	3t	L167/47	
Siam																H93/36	
	2-8-2 + 2-8-2	17×21¾	3-5⅜	185	41666	40·7	—	151	1442	457·5	10·3	81·3	115·4	3960	5t	H26/30	Fuel Capacity=12m^3 wood
Ottoman Railway Company																	
	2-8-0 + 0-8-2	17½×26	4-2½	180	42560	48·5	6-1⅝	202	2489	Nil	14·5	115·4	140·9	5000	8t		
Iranian State Railway																G373/36	
86	4-8-2 + 2-8-4	19·29×25·98	4-5⅛	200	54750	68·25	7-6	278	3334	874	14·75	117·85	201·3	5630	1750g	L306/36	

Chapter 5

Australasia

To the continent of Australasia goes the credit for introducing the Garratt locomotive, not on the mainland but on the island of Tasmania. At various periods most of the railway systems in the continent operated Garratts, and one or two preserved are still capable of use so that Garratts have had 70 years of operation in Australia.

Tasmanian Government Railways

The very first Garratts were two little 0—4—0 + 0—4—0 purchased in 1909 for the North East Dundas Tramway, a 2ft 0in-gauge line which ran from the lead mining town of Zeehan to Williamsford, a distance of seventeen miles. This line ran through an area of thickly-wooded hills and gorges, and included a scenic wooden trestle bridge, on a 5-chain curve, over the Montezuma river. Previous articulated power had consisted of a Hagans 2—6—4—0T, and with an increase in traffic, the two Garratts were purchased from Beyer Peacock.

These differed from all subsequent Garratts in having their cylinders at the inner ends of the

power bogies, an arrangement made to suit the compound expansion adopted, the distance between high- and low-pressure cylinders being shortened thereby. All cylinders had piston valves driven by Walschaerts gear and the plate frames were outside the wheels. An unsuperheated boiler with Belpaire firebox was fitted.

The two engines, classed 'K', remained in service until the closure of the line in 1930, when they sat silently in the deserted engine shed at Zeehan. However, in 1947, number K1 was repurchased by Beyer Peacock and shipped back to England, where it was placed on exhibition at Gorton works, as a museum piece. To commemorate the service given by the locomotive, the railways presented Beyer Peacock with a plaque of Tasmanian Blackwood, carved in the shape of the island and with a likeness of number K1 in relief upon it.

When Beyer Peacock closed their works in 1965, the fate of this historic engine was for a while in the balance, but fortunately it was then purchased by the Festiniog Railway in North Wales, who at one time intended to run it on their

The first fumble towards the eventually successful Garratt — Tasmania's class K, uncharacteristically with compound expansion and cylinders mounted at the inner ends of the bogies. Even on this small

engine the cramped position of inboard-facing cylinders is evident, and no others were built in this form. Beyer Peacock

As a freight plodder, the TGR class L survived longer than its high-spirited express version. Tasmanian Railways

Atlantics are speedy and smooth running, as are four-cylinder locomotives. Combine these features with the Garratt's easy riding, and Tasmania had an engine so swift and smooth running that one derailed due to excessive (and probably unrealised) speed, leading to the type's disfavour. Beyer Peacock

60cm gauge track, this being almost the 2ft gauge to which the locomotive was built. However, the Festiniog's cramped loading gauge would have necessitated extensive structural alterations to the Garratt, and good sense prevailed in not desecrating such a historical locomotive. Recently, K1 has been moved to the National Railway Museum, York, where its future seems secure.

The other locomotive, K2, was sold for scrap.

Following the success of the two narrow-gauge engines, the CME, Mr W. R. Deeble, decided to introduce Garratts on the 3ft 6in main line of the Tasmanian Government Railways, and four engines, two each of Classes 'L' and 'M', were purchased from Beyer Peacock and placed in service in 1912.

Both types were of the same size, and had identical superheated Belpaire boilers, and the same coal and water capacities. Here, however, the similarity ended, for the 'L' class were 2—6—2 + 2—6—2 type, the first of this popular wheel arrangement, and had normal two-cylinder units, with small wheels, for freight service.

The 'M' class, however, were remarkable machines, being 4—4—2 + 2—4—4 engines for express passenger traffic, each unit having four simple-expansion cylinders, thus making them the only eight-cylinder Garratts built. On test, one reached a speed of 55mph, which was regarded as an incredible performance for a 3ft 6in-gauge articulated locomotive. The steady running at this high speed was much commented upon and it may safely be said that these engines did much to establish the Garratt as a highly versatile form of motive power, suitable for all duties.

The smooth running of the eight-cylinder M class, though, was held to be responsible for excessive speed, leading to derailment of the Hobart mail in 1916, and the Garratts fell out of favour, especially for fast passenger work, later taken over by Pacifics. By the Second World War all were out of use, but the two L class freight engines were resuscitated for wartime traffic until replaced by Australian Standard Garratts.

Class & No	Type	B-Peacock Nos	Date built
K1-2	0-4-0 + 0-4-0	5292-93	1909
L1-2	2-6-2 + 2-6-2	5525-26	1912
M1-2	4-4-2 + 2-4-4	5523-24	1912

The four original 3ft 6in-gauge Garratts were officially written off in 1951, although by then they had long been out of use.

The Emu Bay Railway

This railway, also of 3ft 6in gauge, is a mineral line owned by the Electrolytic Zinc Company of Tasmania, and its line includes gradients as steep as 1 in 40, combined with reverse curves of 5 chains radius. Running from the coast at Zeehan to the slopes of Mount Lyell, the railway was built to haul valuable ores such as copper, zinc, pyrites, lead, and silver which are mined there.

Traffic was at first hauled by tank engines, but in 1930 Beyer Peacock delivered three 4-8-2 + 2-8-4 Garratts of very similar design to those supplied to the Kenya Uganda Railway, but with larger water tanks. These performed very satisfactorily, and were eventually joined by three of the Australian Standard Garratts, details of which will be found in Chapter 11.

The line has now been fully dieselised, and the Garratts withdrawn, their building data being as follows:

Emu Bay Nos	Builder	Builders' Nos	Date
12-14	Beyer Peacock	6580—2	1929
16-18	Islington & Clyde	See Chapter 11	

Western Australian Government Railways

This 3ft 6in-gauge system was the first railway on the mainland to use Garratts, and subsequently the railway's Midland Junction works were the first in the Southern Hemisphere to build Garratts. Another 'first' is that the original batch were the pioneer Garratts of a main-line nature to be built, the first class to have more than two locomotives, and they were also the third class of Garratts placed in service.

Of the 2-6-0 + 0-6-2 type, this initial batch used saturated steam, but nevertheless had piston-valve cylinders, with short-lap valves and Z ports. The plate frames were inside the wheels and the connecting rods were long and drove the third pair of coupled wheels in each unit, instituting a standard infrequently strayed from by Beyer Peacock. The boiler had a Belpaire firebox with side-feed clacks and Ramsbottom safety valves.

These engines were used mainly on branch lines in the rural and forest areas of the South West, and had to contend with gradients as steep as 1 in 22, together with 5 chain curves, laid with 45lb rail. Classed 'Ma' at first, the original six engines were soon simply Class 'M', and in 1913—14 were joined by a further seven of similar design but with superheater, classed 'Ms'. One of the Class 'M', No 389, was subsequently superheated and classed 'Ms', but the rest were withdrawn, the last in January 1955.

In 1930, further Garratts being required, an additional ten were put in hand at the railway's

*The original Western Australian Garratt type, class
M, the first Garratt class with more than two
examples.* WAGR

*WAGR's class Ms, the superheated version of the
original class M.* WAGR

Midland Junction workshops, these being similar
again, but with larger coal and water capacities,
and with stove-pipe chimneys instead of the
handsome Beyer Peacock design. They were rated
to haul 590 tons over 1 in 80 gradients. They were
out of service by the 1960s.

Subsequently, the WAGR had some larger
4—8—2 + 2—8—4 Garratts designed by their own
CME and known as the Australian Standard
Garratt, details of which will be found in Chapter
11. Building data are:

Class	Loco Nos	Builder	Builders' Nos	Date
M	388-93	Beyer Peacock	5477-82	1911
Ms	424-30	Beyer Peacock	5665-71	1912
Msa	466-75	Midland Junction	46-55	1930
ASG		See Chapter 11		

Victorian Government Railways

For their 2ft 6in-gauge branches, from Colac to
Crowes and Moe to Walhalla, the VGR purchased
from Beyer Peacock in 1926 two 2—6—0 + 0—6—2
Garratts which probably rank as the most powerful engines ever built for that gauge. Laid with
60lb rails, the lines could take a heavy axle load,
but with 1 in 30 grades and curves of 2 chains.

The engine units of these locomotives had
outside plate frames, all wheels, including the
pony trucks, having outside bearings. Piston-
valve cylinders, slightly inclined, drove the third
pair of driving wheels in each unit, through crank
webs made with integral balance weights. The
Belpaire boiler supplied superheated steam, and
had an air brake pump mounted on the right-hand
side of the smokebox.

(above)   A colourful engine on a colourful train. Earthmoving and other equipment for booming Kenya approaches Changamwe behind No 5934 *Menengai Crater, the last Garratt built for East African Railways.*   A. E. Durrant

(below) Zimbabwe   *Thoroughly international.* 15A Garratt No 389 belongs to Rhodesia Railways, but is seen here hauling a train of South African coaches near Lobatsi, Botswana! Regular running between Bulawayo and Mafeking traversed all three countries on a 968 mile (1,550km) round trip, with two crews and caboose.   A. E. Durrant

The thrice-weekly mixed train from West Nicholson
to Bulawayo gallops through the central African
bush near Eagle Vulture siding, hauled by Rhodesia
14A Garratt No 512.   A. E. Durrant

In service, these engines each replaced two 2—6—2Ts, hauling a 160 ton load compared to the tank's 68 tons, and saving 40 per cent fuel compared to two 2—6—2Ts, this being largely attributable to the Garratt's grate area being about 2½ times that of its predecessor. These lines have now been closed to traffic, but one of the Garratts has been acquired by the 'Puffing Billy' preservation society, and although not yet in working order, this is constantly under review; one day the engine will doubtless be back at work. Puffing Billy has now been renamed the Emerald Tourist Railway.

Numbered G41 and G42, these engines were Beyer Peacock Nos 6267—68 dated 1926.

Australian Portland Cement Co

Impressed, apparently, by the success of the VGR Garratts, the cement company, in 1936, also ordered a Garratt for traffic on their 3ft 6in-gauge line from Fryansford works to their limestone quarry at Batesford, near Geelong, also in Victoria. On this line, 3½ miles long, gradients of 1 in 36 were encountered and curves were 6 chains on the line and 4 chains in sidings. A shuttle service of six wagons totalling 168 tons was operated, a round trip being run every half hour.

Action photographs of Western Australian Garratts are very rare, and this shot of Msa No 499 is predictably taken by a visitor from an Eastern state. W. A. Pearce

Large and chunky for 2ft 6in gauge, Victorian class G on a pulpwood train at Colac. Victorian Railways

Australian Portland Cement Co's 3ft 6in gauge Garratt No 1 at Fryansford, Victoria. W. A. Pearce

The Garratt supplied, which was delivered in April 1936, is described in Beyer Peacock's catalogues as being similar to the VGR 2ft 6in-gauge locomotives. This similarity was very vague indeed, the wheel arrangement being the same and the overall size and power comparable, but in fact, the engine was a WAGR class Ms, modified only in details, such as the provision of a better cab, top feed, and similar variations of a fairly minor nature. In 1939, a further similar locomotive was supplied and finally one of the ill-fated ASG was purchased, this being one of the last of its type to be withdrawn, in 1959. Numbering details are:

APC Co No	Builder	Builders' Nos	Date
1	Beyer Peacock	6794	1936
2	,,	6935	1939
3	See Chapter 11		

Queensland Government Railways

It was largely for this system, which during the second world war was the Australian railway closest to the Far East fighting, that the Australian Standard Garratt was developed. Of 3ft 6in gauge, the axle loads allowed were low, and a powerful engine was needed to cope with the heavy wartime traffic. How the ASG fared may be followed in Chapter 11, from which it will

be seen that the QGR took delivery of their first ASG in September 1943, and eventually ran twenty-three of them, yet withdrew all from service in 1945.

This left a void in the motive power stock, and an order was then placed with Beyer Peacock for thirty 4—8—2 + 2—8—4s of similar size to the ASG, but with slightly larger wheels and to a typical Beyer Peacock post-war design, similar in appearance to, but somewhat smaller than such engines as the East African '60' class. Beyer Peacock being extremely busy at the time, twenty were sub-let to the Société Franco-Belge, being some of the very few continental-built locomotives 'down under'.

These engines, classed simply 'Beyer Garratt', had inside plate frames, roller bearings on the carrying axles, and modern cylinders which were fed with superheated steam from a Belpaire boiler containing arch tubes. Painted red, they were at first used in the Brisbane area, but were later mainly at Rockhampton where they worked the trains from the Callide coalfields. In their time, when they worked the main line to Toowoomba, they hauled air-conditioned expresses, putting up fine performances over heavy gradients. After an artificially short life due to dieselisation (Queensland is now a coal exporter!), the Garratts were withdrawn in the late 1960s, although No 1009 is preserved at the Redbank museum, between Brisbane and Ipswich.

An immaculate Queensland Garratt, in maroon livery, poses on a railfan special. R. N. Redman

Engine Nos	Builder	Builders' Nos	Date
1090-99	Beyer Peacock	7341-50	1951
1000-19	Franco-Belge	2905-24*	1951

*Sub-let from Beyer Peacock, Nos 7433-52

South Australian Railways

For their heavy coal traffic on the 3ft 6in-gauge section from Cockburn to Peterborough, the SAR in the early 1950s found themselves in need of heavier power than the 4—8—0s then in use. The Garratt was an obvious solution, and as a stop-gap measure six of the ASG were purchased from the WAGR at the end of 1951. Details will be found in Chapter 11.

However, by this time, ten adequate Garratts had been ordered from Beyer Peacock and, because of the need for urgent delivery, were sub-contracted to the Société Franco-Belge at Raismes, in France, who built them in 1953. Numbered 400—409, they were in all essentials identical with the East African Railways '60' class, and were thus a development of the War Department Garratts. However, while the EAR Garratts were of metre gauge, built convertible to 3ft 6in, the South Australian locomotives were 3ft 6in gauge, convertible to either 4ft 8½in or 5ft 3in gauges, although this conversion never took place.

The ten Garratts were issued to traffic between July 1953 and February 1954, but were prematurely withdrawn about 1963 due to dieselisation. However, they were not cut up, and in 1968, when the main line was being converted to standard gauge, the diesels were in turn temporarily withdrawn for gauge conversion, and six Garratts plus a number of 4—8—0s were returned to service until January 1970, ending in a blaze of glory when 400 and 401 double-headed a train of ore empties from Port Pirie to Peterborough. Two of these engines have been preserved, No 409 at the Mile End Museum, Adelaide, and 402 as a working exhibit, at the Zig Zag Railway, near Lithgow, NSW.

Beyer Peacock works numbers for the ten engines were 7622—31, the Franco-Belge equivalents being 2973—82, dated 1953.

New South Wales Government Railways

Last in Australasia to adopt the Garratt, this 4ft 8½in-gauge system already had in service some three-cylinder 4—8—2s, Classes D57 and D58, of comparable power, which were built to eliminate double-heading of the older 2—8—0s, Classes D50, D53, and D55, mainly on heavy coal trains. Even so, over the heavy 1 in 42 section from Lithgow to Zig Zag signalbox, these engines were assisted by two 2—8—0s at the front with a further one banking at the rear, making this the most

Not quite a triple header, as the third engine (a Silverton Tramway 4—8—2) is dead, but the two South Australian 400 class Garratts make up for this on a splendid railfan runpast.   W. A. Pearce

spectacular steam operation in Australia. Powerful as these engines were, they were handicapped in their operation by an axle load of nearly 23 tons, and when dieselisation and electrification of the main lines took place in the 1950s, these engines were scrapped, the D58s in 1957 after only seven years of service.

However, before this melancholy event had taken place, the need was seen for a locomotive of similar capacity for the more lightly laid branches, where the axle load was limited to 16 tons. A rigid engine, to achieve this, would need six coupled axles, out of the question due to curvature, hence while the D58s were being built, negotiations were under way with Beyer Peacock to supply sixty Garratts.

The design chosen, a 4—8—4 + 4—8—4, Class AD60, was destined to be the largest and most powerful of Australian steam locomotives and, unfortunately, arrived at a time when dieselisation was well under way. Troubles were experienced with these engines when first delivered in 1952, both with maintenance and in operation, and, with the encouragement of the American diesel interests who were establishing a strong foothold, the order was reduced from sixty to fifty engines, of which the last eight were to be delivered in pieces as spares.

However, the troubles were found to be entirely due to unfamiliarity and were soon overcome,

doubtless to the discomfiture of the *Agents Provocateur Americains*, and many were still in service until the early 1970s, holding the fort on lines too light for the heavy American-inspired diesels. These lines were mainly in the north of NSW from Orange to Dubbo both direct and via Molong, and from Molong to Parkes. They were also found at Newcastle, where they worked colliery branches and even made occasional sorties down the electrified main line to Sydney, when traffic boomed.

Maximum loads of 1500 tons were hauled between Webbs and Dubbo, unassisted over 1 in 100 gradients, but assisted by a 2—8—0 up the 1 in 70 sections. From Molong to Orange, where 1 in 40 gradients have to be surmounted, 900 ton trains were hauled with one 2—8—0 helper, and 1020 tons of heavy minerals, double-headed by two Garratts.

Construction details of the engines were thoroughly modern, and included Commonwealth cast-steel beds on the engine units, Skefco roller

(right) Drama at Fassifern! Hauling coal up 1 in 40, the second Garratt is weakened by bad priming as No 6039, trying to do it all, erupts into a violent slip, all but stalling the train. Maintenance neglect in their last months of service had reduced these proud articulateds to wheezing hulks. Nevertheless, diesels equally mistreated would never have started the train, let alone dragged it over the summit!   A. E. Durrant

74

bearings on all axles and on the main driving crankpins. Modern design piston-valve cylinders were linked to normal Walschaerts valve gear operated by the Hadfield power reverse.

The mechanically-stoked boiler had a round-top firebox which, in the first twenty-five locomotives, contained four arch tubes, and in the remainder, two thermic syphons plus two arch tubes. Rocking grates were fitted, hand operated.

A number of modifications were made after they had been in service, one being an increase in the coal capacity, and another being the fitting of brakes to the inner bogies. Twenty-nine of the 60 class were modified to provide a heavier axle load, with cylinders bored out to give increased tractive effort, and these were given the designation '++'. Also, many were converted to dual control, so that they could be driven cab first with the driver facing the direction of motion. This latter was done at trade union insistence (probably prompted by diesel interests), but in practice drivers usually drove the Garratts facing towards the chimneys!

Garratts lasted to the bitter end of steam in NSW, and indeed, in 1969, when many had been withdrawn, a new 6042 was assembled from spare components to replace the original 6042 which needed heavy repairs. The last ten 60 class were stationed at Broadmeadow shed, Newcastle, from whence they worked coal traffic from Newdell and Newstan collieries, plus general freight along the 'short North' main line to Gosford. The Short North included two particularly severe northbound gradients, the 1 in 40 from Fassifern station, and the longer 1 in 44 from Dora Creek to Hawkmount. Up these, the 60s performed admirably, sometimes solo, but often double-headed with other 'straight' locomotives, or a sister Garratt. The coal trains from Newstan colliery were a regular double-Garratt operation, another spectacular steam show, with 520-odd tons of locomotive straining to heave 1200 tons of coal train over a 1 in 40 hump, from a standing start. Another working in those last days was the short branch from Awaba coal mine to Wangi power station, in the same area, which remained Garratt worked until early 1973, the last regular steam working on any Australian state railway system.

Several Australian publications have made the erroneous claim that the NSW AD60 class were the most powerful steam locomotives in the southern hemisphere. They were certainly the heaviest, but far from being the most powerful, as the following table of comparative dimensions shows. This table rates the various locomotives in order of tractive effort at 85 per cent boiler pressure, and also quotes grate area as a measure of sufficient steaming capacity. One or two classes with high tractive efforts but small

boilers have been omitted from the comparison as being unlikely to achieve their potential.

Country	Class	Tractive Effort (lb @ 85%)	Grate Area (sq ft)	Loco weight (tons)	No of Locos
S. Africa	GL	89130	75	214	8
E. Africa	59	83350	72	252	34
Chile (FCS)		78360	69	187	6
Rhodesia	20/20A	69333	63	225	61
S. Africa	GM/A/AM	68800	63	174 to 192*	136
NSW	AD60	63600	63	264	29

*Plus water cart, about 50 tons.

The AD60 clearly emerges as the sixth most powerful in the southern hemisphere, although the heaviest. Indeed, this great weight was a handicap, a deadweight on steep gradients, detracting much from the drawbar tractive effort, so that on a 1 in 40 gradient, a single South African GL could haul 950 tons, compared with 1200 tons for *two* AD60s. Within the 264 tons total weight of the eventual AD60++ variant, it would have been possible to design a 2—10—2 + 2—10—2 Garratt, with 22 ton axle load (as easily permitted on NSW main lines), which could single handed tackle the 1200 ton trains out of Fassifern which otherwise required two AD60s. The way excess weight dissipated useful tractive effort at the drawbar may be illustrated by a further table:

Locomotive(s)	Two AD60	Single 2-10-2 Garratt
Total weight (tons)	528	264
Total tractive effort (lb)	127200	110000
less		
Rolling resistance @ 10lb/ton	5280	2640
Gradient res. 1 in 40	29570	14785
Total resistance (lb)	34850	17425
Nett drawbar TE	92350	92575

Thus, within their substantial weight, the AD60s had the potential to be the most powerful locomotives in the southern hemisphere, but their original light axle-load specification denied them this distinction, exceeded by five other designs, four of which were African and narrow gauge.

A number of NSW Garratts have been preserved, one with the official collection at Thirlmere, a working example, 6029, at Canberra, plus one or two in the amazing Hunter River collection near Newcastle. It is still, thus,

Engine Nos	B-Peacock Nos	Date	Remarks
6001-25	7473-97	1952	
6026-42	7528-44	1952	
6043-47	7545-49		Delivered as spares
6048-50	*		but not built

*BP Nos 7550-52 allocated to 6048-50, later used on South African Railways Garratts.

A new Garratt locomotive for New Zealand Railways, on a trial run, begins the 1 in 40 climb out of Wellington to Ngaio and Khandallah on 22 February 1929. Evening Post (courtesy J. D. Wilkinson)

possible to witness an AD60 at work, but the absolutely deafening thunder which interrupted lessons at Fassifern's lineside local school has unfortunately passed into history, although several excellent local recordings capture, for those with adequate hi-fi equipment, the eardrum bending cacaphony which accompanied Australia's big show in the days of steam.

New Zealand Government Railways

The 3ft 6in-gauge New Zealand system had a long period of experience with articulated locomotives, commencing in 1872 with some small 0—4—0 + 0—4—0 Fairlies which subsequently amounted to three different classes. They were not too popular, and by the turn of the century had been taken out of service, although a few survived sold out of service until the end of the first war.

The next experience was with a 2—6—6—0T Mallet built to the designs of G. A. Pearson in the railway's Petone workshops. This monstrosity had Vauclain superimposed compound cylinders on each unit, making it an eight-cylinder contrivance and suffered perpetually from mechanical troubles and poor steaming. Built in 1905, it lasted only until 1917 and was then scrapped.

The NZGR's third venture into articulated power, no more successful than the previous two, was with the Garratt type, and was first conceived as early as 1914. However, not until 1928 was an order placed with Beyer Peacock for three 4—6—2 + 2—6—4, to the specifications of the CME, Mr G. S. Lynde. These were the second double Pacific Garratts ever built, and the second and also the last design with three-cylinder units.

Extremely fine looking locomotives, their large round-top boiler almost filling the restricted loading gauge, the plate-framed power bogies had steeply inclined cylinders, the centre cylinder being a little higher than those outside. Walschaerts gear drove the outside piston valves, which had a 1⅛in lap although with only ⅞in steam ports, giving a restricted cut-off, while the centre valve was operated by Gresley 2 to 1 motion. The coal bunker was built on to the boiler frame to accommodate the Duplex mechanical stoker fitted. Front and rear water tanks were mounted on the power units in the normal Garratt fashion.

In service, these engines were a distinct embarrassment, being far too powerful for the couplers in use, while the loads which they could haul were longer than the sidings and passing loops could accommodate. Trouble was also experienced with slipping, due to the low factor of adhesion and also with maintenance on the Gresley gear and the inside motion, both, like the Garratt, unfamiliar to the NZGR staff.

Accordingly, the Garratts saw little work on the North Island main line for which they were designed. In 1936 they were transferred to the South Island where, in the following year, they were dismantled and the engine units used to build six Pacifics, classed 'G' as were the Garratts. However, they retained the mechanical features which had handicapped the Garratts and

were not at all popular, and, in 1955—6, they were the first NZGR main-line locomotives to fall under the onslaught of the diesels.

As Garratts, Class 'G' Nos 98—100, they were built by Beyer Peacock, Nos 6484—86, in 1928.

Although the New Zealand Garratts, as built, were not a success, this in no way detracts from the Garratt's worth, and in the book *The NZR Garratt Story*, E. J. McClaire recounts a number of very interesting proposals made for Garratts to work in New Zealand. There is a very straight-forward double-Pacific Garratt proposed by Beyer Peacock, rather like the Nigerian loco-motives, or a South African GF, which would undoubtedly have been more useful than the G class as built. For the Rimutaka incline, worked on the Fell central rail system, there were a variety of extremely interesting Garratt proposals of specialised and unconventional design, which are reproduced here by courtesy of the author of this very interesting book, and by its publishers, the New Zealand Railway and Locomotive Society Inc.

As straight, adhesion only, Garratts, North British proposed a 2—6—0 + 0—6—2 design, rather similar to South Africa's GA. This was developed into a double 0—8—0, total adhesion, using the same boiler, and probably more useful. Meanwhile, Beyer Peacock were not idling, and in

New Zealand's Rimutaka incline, worked by Fell centre rail 0—4—2T, with up to five per train, attracted several Garratt proposals for more economic working. This straight 0—6—0 + 0—6—0

Garratt with Fell wheels and cylinders on each unit would have equalled about three of the standard tank engines in haulage capacity.

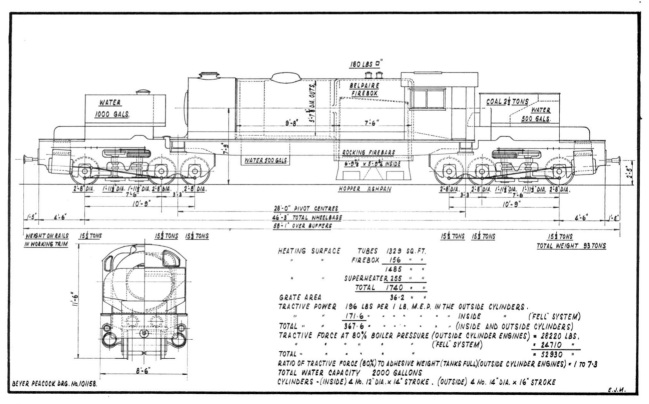

1931 produced a design for an 0—6—0 + 0—6—0 in which each unit was geared, to provide more even tractive effort. This followed an earlier proposal for an 0—6—0 + 0—6—0 in which each unit had normal adhesion plus Fell central rail drive, to provide in one locomotive the power of about three of the usual Fell 0—4—2T engines. Also in 1931, Vulcan Foundry proposed an interesting cross-breed design, with Garratt style front and rear tanks, but both engine units driven by a single pair of cylinders via a central propellor shaft, rather like a Heisler. If nothing else, these various proposals showed that the Garratt principle exhibited considerable versatility in its possible interpretation of execution.

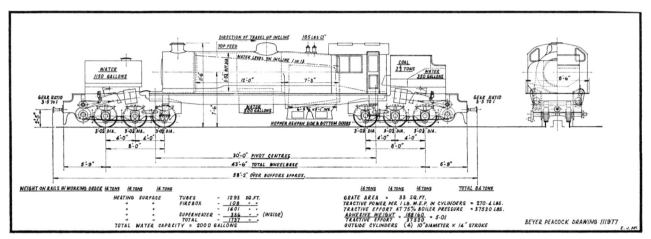

An alternative Beyer Peacock proposal for Rimutaka was an adhesion-only Garratt with geared transmission to give more even torque, with better adhesion.

The third Rimutaka proposal, by Vulcan Foundry in 1931, while outwardly of Garratt configuration, featured two cylinders mounted on the boiler unit, driving the engine units by a geared shaft. In this respect, the locomotive was basically of the Climax type, and may be considered a hybrid Climax-Garratt. These three diagrams, reproduced from The NZR Garratt Story, *by kind permission of the author and publishers (see bibliography) illustrate some of the unused options available for using the basic Garratt articulation principle.*

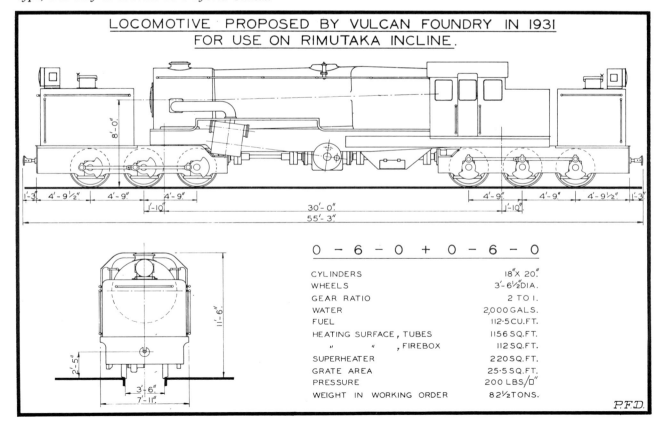

AUSTRALASIA

Class	Type	Cylinders Dia × Stroke (in)	Coupled Wheel Dia (ft in)	Boiler Press (psi)	Tract Effort @ 75% (lb)	Grate Area sq ft	Max Boiler Dia (Outs) ft in	Heating Surface (sq ft) Fire-box	Tubes	Super-heater	Weights in Working Order (Tons) Max Axle	Ad-hesive	Total	Water Cpty (Gal)	Fuel Cpty (Tons /Gal)	Literature Reference
Tasmanian Government Railways																
K	0-4-0 + 0-4-0	(2) 11×16 (2) 17×16	2-7½	195	14380	14·8	3-11⅛	60	568	Nil	8·75	33·54	33·54	840	1t	L372/23
L	2-6-2 + 2-6-2	15×22	3-6	160	27200	33·9	5-4½	155·5	1530·5	333	9·5	56·8	90·0	3000	4t	L205/12
M	4-4-2 + 2-4-4	(8) 12×20	5-0	160	23000	33·9	5-4½	155·5	1530·5	333	12·0	48·0	94·55	3000	4t	L204/12
Western Australian Government Railways																
M	2-6-0 + 0-6-2	12½×20	3-3	175	21030	22·6	Ins 4-10$\frac{13}{16}$	107	1233	Nil	9·0	52·35	66·5	2000	2t	L28/12
Ms	2-6-0 + 0-6-2	13¼×20	3-3	160	21600	22·6	Ins 4-10$\frac{13}{16}$	107	959·5	180	9·35	55·45	69·8	2000	3t	
Msa	2-6-0 + 0-6-2	13¼×20	3-3	160	21600	27·0	Ins 4-10$\frac{13}{16}$	116	970	180	10·0	60·0	74·0	2000	4t	L343/31
Victorian Government Railways																
G	2-6-0 + 0-6-2	13¼×18	3-0	180	23690	22·6	5-0	99	951	180	9·45	55·35	69·0	1680	3·5t	L160/26
South Australian Railways																
400	4-8-2 + 2-8-4	16×24	4-0	200	38400	48·75	6-0	193	1779	370	10·67	84·9	149·0	3700	Oil 6t	
Queensland Government Railways																
	4-8-2 + 2-8-4	13¾×26	4-3	200	29900	39	5-4½	178	1490	453	9·65	77·1	136·75	3800	6t	L112/50
New South Wales Government Railways																
AD60	4-8-4 + 4-8-4	19¼×26 19⅞×26*	4-7	200	52700 56020*	63·5	7-3	238	2792	750	16·0	128·0	260·0 264·5*	9350	14t	L137/52 **As altered*
New Zealand Government Railways																
G	4-6-2 + 2-6-4	(6) 16½×24	4-9	200	51580	58·2	6-6	245	2223	542	14·9	87·7	145·8	4000	6t	L6/29
Emu Bay Railway																
	4-8-2 + 2-8-4	16½×22	3-7	180	37610	43·6	6-0	174	1863	380	10·5	84·0	132·65	5250	6t	
Australian Portland Cement Co																
	2-6-0 + 0-6-2	13¼×20	3-3	180	24300	22·6	5-0	107	959·9	245·5	9·4	55·4	71·0	2000	3t	L144/36

Note: For Australian Standard Garratt see Chapter 11

Chapter 6

America

As far as the American Continent goes, only the countries south of the Panama used Garratts, though as noted in Chapter 2, they were seriously considered in the USA and manufacturing rights were taken up by the American Locomotive Company. These rights were never used however, either for domestic or export locomotives.

NORTH AMERICA

When the original volume of *The Garratt Locomotive* appeared, North America featured only as a supplier and onetime interested prospector of the Garratt principle. We may now recount the fact that there is one Garratt operating in the USA, albeit a secondhand narrow gauge (2ft) example from South Africa, and far removed from the enormous machines once envisaged by Beyer Peacock and Alco, who looked into the possibilities of building 'Super-Garratts' for the American market.

Hempstead and Northern Railroad, Texas

There are many privately-owned steam locomotives in the world today, but it goes to a Texan to run perhaps the only privately-operated Garratt. One might expect a Texan to run to an SAR GL, or East African 59, but this little two foot gauge NGG 13, with its train of genuine SAR rolling stock can claim to be unique on the North American continent.

Before that though, American manufactured cast steel beds were supplied for British and Continental-built Garratts for various parts of Africa and Australia, so that the USA had a very real, if peripheral, interest in the Garratt locomotive. At one time, America had a more active interest in the Garratt principle, and when Beyer Peacock evolved the Mallet Garratt, or Super-Garratt, Alco took up the manufacturing rights of this intriguing possibility. No Super-Garratt was ever built, but the Beyer Peacock proposal for a 2—6—6—2 + 2—6—6—2 was described in the present author's book *The Mallet Locomotive*, and compared with contemporary American leviathans. Later, an article in the American *Trains* magazine expanded on the original Beyer Peacock proposal to include the possibility of a 4—8—8—4 + 4—8—8—4 double 'Big Boy', and using the extremes of proven steam technology, a 2—12—12—2 + 2—12—12—2 Super Garratt of over 400,000lb (1780kN) starting tractive effort. If nothing else, these projects show that the full potential of steam traction has never been realised, and interesting details of these further possibilities may be found in the special Appendix.

SOUTH AMERICA

Numerous railways in South America used Garratts, although they were generally obtained for special duties and were not used as the standard form of motive power as in Africa. A wide variety of types, from 0—4—0 + 0—4—0 to 4—8—2 + 2—8—4, was represented, together with a range of gauges from 3ft 0in to 5ft 6in. While most were mountain sloggers, duties covered a wide sphere from industrial to express work.

Argentina

In the 1960s, railways in Argentina were in a very run down state, and with no money to buy spares for diesels, many steam locomotives were returned to service, although by then, unfortunately, virtually all the various Garratt types had been scrapped. *South American Steam*, published in 1970, lists no Garratts, and one assumes that they were largely scrapped from the mid-1950s to mid-1960s, when diesels started taking over the more onerous duties. The various railways with their descriptively geographical names, were nationalised in 1956, and given names of military significance, allocated by rail gauge. One is inclined to imagine the scurrilous notion of the respective General's corpulence being the deciding factor in whether he was allocated a broad, standard, or narrow gauge railway!

Buenos Aires & Pacific Railway (now Ferrocarril General San Martin)

This 5ft 6in-gauge railway had one class of Garratt, the 4—8—2 + 2—8—4, of which only four were built, for the subsidiary Grande Occidentale Argentine or Great Western of Argentine Railway. Rather fine looking engines with wheels of fairly large diameter, they ran on the Villa Mercedes to Villa Dolores branch, which had an axle load restriction of 14·2 tons. Originally coal burners, they were converted to burn oil in 1941.

"BEYER-GARRATT" LOCOMOTIVES for SOUTH AMERICA

Tractive effort (75% B.P.) 44,490 lbs.　　　　　　　　Maximum axle load 14 tons.

Three **"BEYER-GARRATT"** Patent Articulated LOCOMOTIVES of the above type have recently been delivered from our Works to the BUENOS AYRES & PACIFIC RAILWAY COMPANY (*Gran Oeste Argentina*) for branch line Service.

For the Gran Oeste Argentina *section of the Buenos Aires Pacific, Beyer Peacock built these handsome Garratts for branch line service.* Beyer Peacock

One was exhibited at the British Empire Exhibition at Buenos Aires in 1931.

Constructionally, they were plate-framed engines, with modern design piston-valve cylinders, and Walschaerts valve gear. The superheated boiler had a Belpaire firebox containing thermic symphons, and as coal burners they were hand fired. All are now scrapped. Their BAP numbers were 951—954, Beyer Peacock 6532—34 of 1930, and 6715 of 1931.

Buenos Aires Great Southern Railway (now Ferrocarril General Roca)

This line, also 5ft 6in gauge, had twelve 4—8—2 + 2—8—4s with a low axle load, for working the lightly laid Bahia Blanca to Neuquen line, and the Toay branch. On this flat country, their main use was in increasing train weights and thus reducing line occupancy, loads of up to 1700 tons being taken.

A Buenos Aires Great Southern Garratt outside the workshops after overhaul. Author's collection

Similar to, but smaller than the BAP engines, they had old-type Z-ported cylinders, lacked thermic syphons, and were oil burning as built by Beyer Peacock in 1928, the works numbers being 6417—28 and the running numbers 4851—62. All these are now scrapped.

Cordoba Central Railway (now Ferrocarril General Belgrano)

The General Belgrano Railway covers all the metre-gauge lines in the Argentine Republic, and the Cordoba Central was a constituent of today's railway. For this line, in 1929, Beyer Peacock built ten 4—8—2 + 2—8—4s which were more powerful than either of the 5ft 6in-gauge classes! Almost identical to those built slightly earlier for the FCAB, the principal difference was in the use of coal as a fuel.

Originally used on the main line between Alta Cordoba, Quilino, and Frias, where they handled 1200 ton trains over 1 in 80 gradients, they were also used on the Los Sauces branch which has 1 in 40 gradients and severe curvature. These engines became class E11 on the Belgrano system, the letter 'E' denoting *locomotora Especial*, a nomenclature including ten-coupled, articulated, and rack types for the heaviest duties. The author has been unable to locate the Los Sauces branch mentioned in Beyer Peacock's literature; it does not appear in the 1931 timetable map of the system, although it could have been a freight only line. In Belgrano days, the author was informed (without confirmation), they were used on the heavily graded line from Jujuy to the Bolivian border, especially between Léon and Volcan, where there is a rack and adhesion section, worked for many years by the class E20 0—8—2T rack engines, and later the gigantic E24

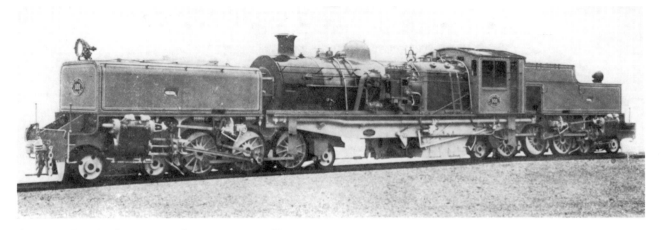

A double-Pacific Garratt for the metre gauge Buenos Aires Midland Railway. Beyer Peacock

0—12—2T. Our informant said that rack and Garratt locomotives were used together, one as banker, and the mind rather boggles at the spectacle of a freight blasting out of the river gorge with a large Garratt leading and a rack 0—12—2T shoving hard at the rear!

On both the Cordoba Central, and the Belgrano, the engines bore numbers 1511—20, and they were Beyer Peacock 6550—59 of 1929.

Buenos Aires Midland Railway
(now Ferrocarril General Belgrano)

Two 4—6—2 + 2—6—4 Garratts were built for this line by Beyer Peacock in 1929, to the same general design as a contemporary pair built for the Leopoldina Railway in Brazil. They were employed mainly on wheat trains, hauling 1600 tons on a level track at 25mph. However, they were not repeated, and during the Second World War one was loaned to the FCAB, indicating that even then full employment could not be found for them. As far as can be ascertained, these two engines did not last long enough to receive Belgrano numbers or classification.

These plate-framed, piston-valve jobs, with Belpaire boilers were FCM Nos 101—102, Beyer Peacock 6570—71 of 1929.

Transandine Railway
(now Ferrocarril General Belgrano)

This metre-gauge line is extremely spectacular, crossing the Andes from Mendoza in the Argentine to Los Andes in Chile, reaching an altitude of 10,400ft in the process, the summit being in a tunnel, under the frontier between the two countries. On the steepest section, rack-and-adhesion locomotives were used, including some remarkable Kitson-Meyers with adhesion on one bogie and rack on the other.

On the lowest stretches, where the gradients were a mere 1 in 40, 2—6—2T and 2—8—4T were used until 1929 when Beyer Peacock supplied four 2—6—2 + 2—6—2 Garratts based upon those supplied to the New Cape Central Railway in South Africa, but with a larger firebox in view of the harder steaming involved. During a period of five years when the line was washed away by floods, two of the Garratts were isolated, and the other two used elsewhere, such as the Guemes-La Quiaca line where, over a 1 in 11 gradient, 380 ton trains were moved, hauled by a rack-and-adhesion engine and banked by a Garratt! The two Garratts eventually returned to their original section, but are now replaced by diesels.

Transandine Nos 61—64, later Belgrano class E12, No 1561—4, were Beyer Peacock numbers 6543—46 of 1930.

The Entre Rios and Argentine North Eastern Railways (FCER and FCNEA)
(now Ferrocarril General Urquiza)

This particular General was allocated the 4ft 8½in-gauge railways in the Argentine, of which the above two were operated by the same management and used Garratts of the same designs. These were the first Garratts used in the Argentine, and special permission from the Argentine Railways Board had to be obtained before they could be purchased.

An interesting paper which was read before the South American Centre of the Institution of Locomotive Engineers in 1926 (see Bibliography) describes how the railways in the province of Entre Rios, being standard gauge, were cut off from Buenos Aires which was served by 5ft 6in-gauge lines, and produce could only be marketed if it were transhipped to boats, an expensive process, raising prices to an uncompetitive level.

Hence, train ferries were introduced, connecting the railway with the 'Tranvia Rural' or local tramway, which happened to be of 4ft 8½in

Entre Rios Railway 2—6—0 + 0—6—2 standard gauge Garratt. Beyer Peacock

Entre Rios Railway double Atlantic Garratt, one of ten built for this and the associated North Eastern Railway of Argentina. Beyer Peacock

gauge, and light Garratts were introduced in order to convey trains of reasonable weight over the light track.

First built was a batch of three 2—6—0 + 0—6—2s for the FCNEA, in 1925, and these were of much the same proportions as one would expect to find on a substantially narrower gauge, the driving wheels being, for example, only 3ft 9in diameter. However, they proved capable of hauling heavier loads than the 2—8—0s previously employed, saving fuel into the bargain, and hence were deemed a great success. As was Beyer Peacock's practice at the time, they were plate-framed machines with old-type, Z-ported, piston-valve cylinders, steam distribution from the superheated Belpaire boiler being effected by Walschaerts gear.

A year's service was sufficient to prove their worth, whereupon further orders were placed with Beyer Peacock, covering additional engines of the same type for both the FCNEA and the FCER. Furthermore, a 2—4—2 + 2—4—2 version was considered for passenger work, and this finally came out as a double Atlantic, with improved straight-ported cylinders and redesigned motion. Five of these were built for the FCER, followed by another five for the FCNEA.

These standard gauge Garratts were the last to exist, if not to work, in Argentina, and from time to time were loaned to the Paraguayan railways, often short of power because of inadequate maintenance. In 1977, one of the 4—4—2 + 2—4—4s was reported to be rotting away in the Paraguayan railway workshops, undoubtedly the last of its type in existence.

Building data for these engines are:

Railway	Type	Running Nos	Beyer Peacock Nos	Date
FCNEA	2-6-0 + 0-6-2	101-103	6238-40	1925
FCNEA	2-6-0 + 0-6-2	104-107	6349-52	1927
FCER	2-6-0 + 0-6-2	401-405	6355-59	1927
FCER	4-4-2 + 2-4-4	101-105	6360-64	1927
FCNEA	4-4-2 + 2-4-4	108-110*	6645-47	1930

*Later 201-203.

A 4—6—2 + 2—6—4 Garratt shown in service on the Leopoldina Railway, Brazil. Author's collection

A particularly interesting special purpose Garratt design for Brazil's Leopoldina Railway, featuring the unique 2—4—2 + 2—4—2 wheel arrangement, poppet valves, and oversize grate for low quality, high ash, coal. Beyer Peacock

Brazil

Mogyana Railway
(Cia. Mogiana des Estradas de Ferro)

This metre-gauge line was the first railway in South America to use Garratts, and it used a wheel arrangement, 4—6—0 + 0—6—4, which was never repeated by Beyer Peacock, although used once elsewhere, the 2—6—2 + 2—6—2 or 4—6—2 + 2—6—4 being better vehicles, easier on the track.

The two original Mogyana engines were saturated-steam jobs, with inside plate frames and Belpaire boilers, and were followed two years later by three similar engines which were, however, superheated and with piston valves. The five engines survived both world wars but, as the railway is now dieselised the Garratts are withdrawn.

Building data are:

Running Nos	Beyer Peacock Nos	Date
Not known	5529-30	1912
189-91	5787-89	1914

Leopoldina Railway
(Estrada de Ferro Leopoldina)

This is one of the major Garratt users in South America and is of metre gauge. With the Midland of Buenos Aires system in the Argentine, it started with two 4—6—2 + 2—6—4s, the designs for the two railways being almost identical, having plate frames with Walschaerts-driven piston valves, and superheated Belpaire boilers.

The first two engines were built for passenger work on the stretch from Campos to Victoria, the ruling gradient being 3 per cent with curves of 80 metres radius. Following good results in service,

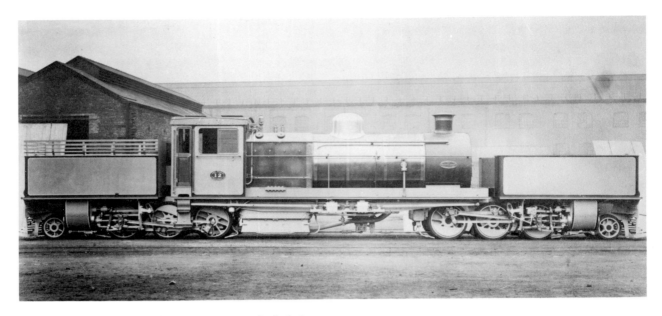

*São Paulo Railway's modest metre gauge 2—6—0 +
0—6—2 led to further and far more ambitious ventures
into Garratt operation.* Beyer Peacock

the engines being capable of hauling 75 per cent
greater loads than the 4—6—2 tender engines,
further orders for the same class were placed over
a period of seventeen years.

In between these orders, a requirement arose
for increased power on the Cantagallo branch,
from Portella to Cordiero, which also had 3 per
cent gradients, together with curves as sharp as
30 metres radius. Four-coupled engines were the
most permitted on the branch, 0—4—2T being
previously employed, and to double the loads of
these, four 2—4—2 + 2—4—2 Garratts were
supplied during the second world war. Despite
these general restrictions, plus a severe axle load
limit, the design evolved was able to include a
large Belpaire firebox, capable of burning low-
grade local coal with a 40 per cent ash content,
using rocking grates and self-cleaning ashpans,
while a free-running design was ensured by the
inclusion of oscillating cam poppet valves,
actuated by Walschaerts gear, and by roller
bearings on the pony truck axles. Other details
were conventional, with plate frames. Later, like
many other Leopoldina engines, they have been
fired with wood, and have also strayed off their
original line.

Building data of Leopoldina Garratts are:

Type	Running Nos	Beyer Peacock Nos	Date
2-4-2 + 2-4-2	400-403	6976-79	1943
4-6-2 + 2-6-4	380-81	6572-73	1929
,, ,,	382-87	6845-50	1937
,, ,,	388-95	7026-33	1943

All are now scrapped.

São Paulo Railway
(Estrada de Ferro Santos a Jundiai)

This railway, whose main line was of 5ft 3in
gauge but had a metre-gauge branch, had some
very interesting operating problems, particularly
on the broad gauge, but it was on the metre-gauge
Bragantina branch that Garratts were first introduced, in 1913. This branch left the main line at
Campo Limpo, and ran to Vangem with a branch
to Praciai, the gradients encountered being as
steep as 1 in 30.

The initial Garratt, a 2—6—0 + 0—6—2, was
typical of Beyer Peacock's practice at the time,
with superheated Belpaire boiler and Z-ported,
piston-valve cylinders. It successfully hauled the
heaviest freight on the system and was joined in
1936 by a similar engine, differing only in minor
details which nevertheless received a fresh
classification.

The 5ft 3in-gauge line from the port of Santos
runs inland to São Paulo, hence the original name
of this once British-owned railway, and thence to
Jundiahy, where it connected with the Paulista
and Sorocobaña railways. The first section from
Santos to Piassaguera was lightly laid, had very
weak bridges, and was an operating problem in
itself. Then, to Alto de Serra an escarpment was
climbed by means of a rope-worked incline, using
also small 0—4—0T tram engines for braking and
additional power. From the summit the main line
proper started running, as described, to
Jundiahy.

As traffic developed, it became imperative that
increased power be obtained, eight-coupled
wheels being necessary in order to handle 1000
ton trains with a maximum axle load of 14 tons.

(above) The wild gorge between Wankie and the Lukosi river is close by the National park, and is frequented by elephant. At roughly hourly intervals, the African peace is disturbed by massive Garratts thundering out on coal trains, or rumbling in on empties. Class 20A No 747, due to be named Jumbo, heads a coal train in 1979, when a coachload of armed guards formed part of every train.   A. E. Durrant

(right) During heavy traffic, limestone trains from Colleen Bawn dropped excess loads at Balla Balla, where the grade steepened. A daily trip working, often double headed, picked up these loads, as seen near Bushtick, with RR 14A and 16A Garratts.
A. E. Durrant

Victoria Falls is undoubtably the major natural wonder in Africa. Because of the imagination of Cecil Rhodes, the railway bridge crosses within sight of the cataract, completely dwarfing a massive 20A Garratt and its train.   A. E. Durrant

For the coastal section to and from Santos, the São Paulo Railway used three 2—4—0 + 0—4—2 mixed traffic Garratts. F.C. Santos a Jundiahy

However, weak bridges prevented the concentrated weight of a normal locomotive from being accepted, and Beyer Peacock designed a neat 2—4—0 + 0—4—2 Garratt, which spread the weight over a wheelbase of 47ft 10in. Built in 1915, these plate-framed, superheated, piston-valve engines, with their Belpaire fireboxes and Walschaerts valve gear, lasted until 1950, and dieselisation. Shuttling back and forth over their few miles of lower section, they made seven or eight round trips a day over this busy stretch.

We now come to the São Paulo's largest and most numerous class of Garratts, and a class which made history. Until their arrival upon the scene, the Garratt had been a mountain slogger or branch-line engine, with wheels never exceeding, and rarely attaining, five feet in diameter. However, the São Paulo, being thoroughly satisfied with their existing Garratts, decided that the type could be profitably used to provide increased power on their main line, where compound 4—6—0s were the largest express engines available. With an 18½ ton axle load permissible, a very large engine was designed, with 5ft 6in wheels, unprecedented in a Garratt, the first such machine built for express traffic.

Design features were as for the 2—4—0 + 0—4—2 except that improved cylinder design, with straight ports, was included, and with their large Belpaire boiler towering over the low front tanks, these 2—6—2 + 2—6—2s were most imposing machines indeed. Their presence enabled trains of 500 tons to be scheduled at an

average speed of 40mph over a distance, start to stop, of thirty-seven miles, during which 60mph was attained, these being the first articulated locomotives in the world to be scheduled to run regularly at such speeds.

After only four years in service, a start was made to convert these engines into 4—6—2 + 2—6—4, the reason given being to increase the water capacity. This was, however, a rather expensive way of going about it, for the alteration involved new wheelsets, bogie frames, main frame extensions, plus new connecting and eccentric rods, apart from the extended tanks. As the additional water capacity thus gained was but 900 gal, the author suspects an additional factor behind the rebuilding, probably some unsteadiness at speed requiring the stabilising influence of a leading bogie.

Whatever the real reason behind the change, it proved adequate, and as double Pacifics the engines remained at work until replaced by electrification in 1950.

The São Paulo Garratts were built as below:

Gauge	Class	Type	Running Nos	Beyer Peacock Nos	Date
Metre	U	2-6-0 + 0-6-2	8	5664	1913
„	V	2-6-0 + 0-6-2	12	6795	1936
5ft 3in	Q	2-4-0 + 0-4-2	155-157	5892-94	1915
„	R1	2-6-2 + 2-6-2	160-165	6367-72	1927
„	R2	4-6-2 + 2-6-4 later			

Shown as first supplied, São Paulo Railway's express Garratt, with 2—6—2 + 2—6—2 wheel arrangement.
Beyer Peacock

Viçáo Ferrea do Rio Grande do Sul

This metre-gauge railway seems to have made a deliberate attempt to compare the merits of the Garratt type with modern simple expansion Mallets, having ordered both types of articulateds from Henschel in the 1920s. However, the two types built were not strictly comparable, the Mallets being the larger engines all round, and were more purely freight engines, while the ten Garratts, delivered in 1931, had larger wheels and lighter axle loads, making them suitable for branch line mixed traffic work.

Built on bar frames, these 4—6—2 + 2—6—4s had round-top fireboxes containing thermic syphons, and the boiler barrels had two domes, the forward one containing the top feed apparatus. The front tank was of a curious boat-shaped cross section, while the rear tank/bunker was of an equally strange section, probably best

Altered to double-Pacifics, the São Paulo express Garratts as they spent most of their working lives.
Beyer Peacock

described as pagoda shaped. When built, they were used on the Porto Alegre to Santa Maria line but with the general dieselisation in Brazil they became redundant, and some were sent to the Donna Teresa Cristina line, supplementing their small Mallets, until much more effective 2—10—4s became available from the Central of Brazil. On the EFDTC, memories of the Garratts were unhappy, and when further steam power was required in the late 1970s, Garratts from, say, East Africa, were rejected in favour of simpler, and certainly more easily shipped, 2—10—2s from Argentina. VFRGS Nos were 901—10, Henschel 22047—056 of 1931.

Porto Feliz Sugar Co, and Piracicaba Sugar Co

The above were possibly one and the same concern, or at least had the same owners. Two Garratts, identical in all main respects, were built by St Léonard for sugar tram working in Brazil, on metre gauge. Both were 0—4—0 + 0—4—0 with side tanks and spark arresting chimneys, and generally similar in detail to the miniscule Garratts built for the Mayumbe Railway in the Belgian Congo, and the Zaccar Mines line in Algeria. Both were supplied to an agent, MM Allain et Fils, of Paris, the first to Sucrerie de Porto Feliz, and the second to Sucrerie de Piracicaba, the latter being in the province of Sao Paulo. For fifty years they hauled sugar cane, unseen and unrecorded by locomotive enthusiasts, until their remarkable survival was documented in the *World of South American Steam*, published 1973, by which time both were at Piracicaba. Even more remarkable, the later information indicates that the engines changed

*Sucrerie de Piracicaba, Brazil, metre gauge, wood-
burning Garratt with spark arresting chimney and
side tanks. July 1970.* Jeremy Wiseman

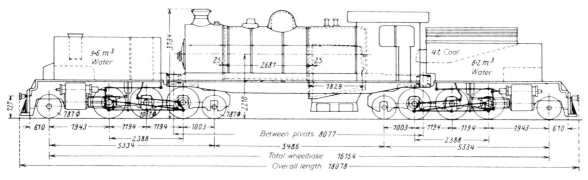

*2—6—2 + 2—6—2 Garratt of the Great Western Railway,
Brazil.*

identities, or at least works plates. The builder's
information gives:

St.L. 2091/27 Porto Feliz. Loco No 5 on works
photo.
St.L. 2108/ Piracicaba.

The later recorded data provides:
St.L. — /(27) Piracicaba No 6.
St.L. 2091/27 Piracicaba No 7.

Anyone who is able to shed further light on this
minor, if fascinating, South American locomotive
mystery, will be welcomed by the author.

Great Western of Brazil Railway

This metre-gauge concern took delivery of its
first two Garratts from Armstrong Whitworth in
1928, it being that company's first of two orders
for Garratts. The engines themselves, however,
bore every appearance of being a Beyer Peacock
design, and were presumably built under licence.
They were very similar to South African Railways' GC design (the dimensions varied slightly),
but had smaller cylinders and higher boiler
pressure.

Just before the Second World War, the railway
ordered a further four much larger machines of
the 4—8—2 + 2—8—4 type from Beyer Peacock.
These were delayed due to the war, but as will be
seen from Chapter 11, formed a basis upon which
a highly successful class was evolved, being used
on a number of lines throughout the world.

After the war the engines were sub-let to
Henschel's plus a further two which were

Rede Ferroviaria do Nordeste Brazil, Henschel Garratt on a trial train crossing a river bridge.
Author's collection

required, and these were delivered to the Rede Ferroviaria do Noroeste, or North Eastern Railway, as the railway had become. All are now withdrawn from service, but one of the Henschel engines has been preserved.

Building data are:

Running Nos	Builder	Builders' Nos	Date
238-39, later 601-2	Armstrong Whitworth	1024-25	1929
610-15	Henschel*	25257-62*	1952

*Originally Beyer Peacock 6966-69 and 7136-37.

Bolivia

Antofagasta (Bolivia) and Chile Railway (FCAB)

This international railway, running from Antofogasta on the Chilean coast, over the Andes, and into Bolivia was, like all Andean railways, extremely difficult to operate. The original line had been built to 2ft 6in gauge, but the inadequacies of this gauge, plus the break of gauge where it connected with other lines made the conversion to metre gauge inevitable. The Uyuni-Oruro section was widened in 1916, and the remaining narrow sections converted by 1928. The main line out of Antofogasta commenced with a screaming climb of 3 per cent (1 in 33) for 38km, to Portezuelo, after which the remaining 330km to Ascotan, where the *Altiplano* was

reached at an altitude of 4000 metres (13,000ft), by 2·2 per cent (1 in 45) grades. Despite the severity of this climb, even more hard work was needed on the branches, where longer sections of 3 per cent gradients were situated against the loads. Between Potosi and Rio Mulato, the line attains an altitude, at Condor, of 4788m, or 15,705ft, the highest metre gauge summit in the world. Thus, it was on the branches, rather than the main line, that articulateds were mainly used, and Beyer Peacock were well entrenched in this field.

The first batch were rather unusual, both in design and origin, being Kitson-Meyers built by Beyer Peacock! Although the Beyer Garratt was, by 1913, fairly well established, there were few in South America, where the Kitson-Meyer was well entrenched on Andean railways. Therefore, although Beyer Peacock undoubtably tried to sell Garratts, they eventually had to settle for the supply of six Kitson-Meyers. These were of a unique design, being 2—6—0 + 2—6—0s arranged to run bunker and cab first. Fuel supplies only were carried on the locomotive, with water carried in an auxiliary cylindrical tank.

By the time further articulateds were required, the Garratt was well established, and Beyer Peacock, in 1929, built three large 4—8—2 + 2—8—4s weighing 170 tons apiece, with 13 ton axle load. They had bar frames, Walschaerts driven piston valves, and Belpaire fireboxes for oil burning, and worked on the Potosi branch. During the Second World War, further Garratts were needed, and from Argentina were hired the

LARGEST METRE GAUGE LOCOMOTIVE IN THE WORLD.

Tractive Effort @ 75% B.P. 48,700 lbs.   65 lb. Rail.   Maximum Axle Load 13 Tons.

Cylinders (4)	Heating Surface : Tubes ... 2,647 sq. ft.	Water Capacity ... ... 5,000 Gallons.
Diameter ... ... 18 in.	Firebox ... 217 do.	Fuel Capacity (Oil) ... 1,670 do.
Stroke ... ... 26 in.	Superheater 593 do.	Adhesive Weight ... ... 104·15 Tons.
Boiler Pressure ... 185 lbs. /sq. in.	Total ... 3,457 do.	Factor of Adhesion ... ... 4·8.
Coupled Wheel diameter 4 ft. 0 in.	Grate Area ... ... 55 sq. ft.	Total Weight, in working order, 169·65 Tons.

Three "**BEYER - GARRATTS**" of the above type have recently been designed and manufactured at our Works for the **Antofagasta (Chili) & Bolivia Railway,** and are the most powerful locomotives ever constructed for service on the Metre Gauge.

These Engines, which are designed for operating on long 3% grades compensated for curves of 100 metres radius, are fitted with bar frames, "Westinghouse" brakes, steam sanding, Superheater Co.'s superheater with M.L.S. multiple valve regulator and header, and Hopkinson Ferranti type stop valve, "Weir" feed-water heater and pump, steam reversing gear, oil firing arrangement, etc.

BEYER PEACOCK & CO., LIMITED
GORTON FOUNDRY, MANCHESTER.
LONDON OFFICE: ABBEY HOUSE, WESTMINSTER.

Telegrams : " Loco, Gorton."
Telegrams : " Folgore, Sowest."

Telephone : Central 5663-5664.
Telephone : Victoria 8082.

(above) Beyer Peacock's advertisement for this FCAB Garratt, built in 1929, claims it as the largest metre gauge locomotive in the world. Subsequent holders of this title were also Garratts. Beyer Peacock

(below) Modernised, postwar FCAB Garratt, lettered for the FCLPA after nationalisation by Bolivia. Howard S. Patrick

69,150 lbs. T.P. @ 75% on 18 tons Axle-load.

Until overtaken by the South African GL class, these Nitrate Railways standard gauge Garratts were the most powerful locomotives in the Southern Hemisphere. Beyer Peacock

two 4—6—2 + 2—6—4s from the BA Midland, plus further large engines from the Cordoba Central, these latter being similar to the FCAB engines. After the war, the hired engines were returned to their owners, and six further Garratts ordered from Beyer Peacock, generally similar to the original design, but differing externally in having the latest pattern streamlined tanks and bunkers.

In 1959, the Bolivian section of the line, including the Garratts, was nationalised by the Bolivian government, and renamed the Ferrocarril La Paz Antofogasta, ie the same name reversed to suit the new seat of government! Later, the various railways were unified to the FF.CC de Bolivia, and the Garratts included in a renumbering scheme which may or may not have been carried out on all the Garratts. They were later named. Details are:

FCAB Nos	FF.CC Nos	Name	Beyer Peacock Nos	Date
390	900	*Choroloque*	6524	1929
391	901	*Illampu*	6525	1929
392	902	*Kosuna*	6526	1929
393	903	*Huayna Potosi*	7420	1950
394	904	*San Vicente*	7421	1950
395	905	*Illimani*	7422	1950
396	906	*Tumari*	7423	1950
397	907	*Sajama*	7424	1950
398	908	*Tres Cruces*	7425	1950

Chile

Nitrate Railways (Ferrocarril de Salitrero)

This 4ft 8½in-gauge railway which, as its title suggests, was for the haulage of nitrates, was one of the most difficult in the world to operate, rising to 3000ft altitude in only 19½ miles from Iquique on the coast, the summit of this climb being at Las Carpas. The principal gradient is 1 in 25, while a stretch as steep as 23·3 occurs. Furthermore, there is yet another section, where the combination of curves with the gradient equals a straight climb of 1 in 21.

Traffic on this hill section was hauled by two classes of tank engine, some Porter 2—8—2T and Yorkshire Engine Co 4—8—4T, with the same size wheels and cylinders. They could handle loads of 160-180 tons, but as it was desirable to increase the load to 400 tons, Beyer Peacock were entrusted with the design of a 2—8—2 + 2—8—2 Garratt, with the same cylinder and wheel sizes, but working at a higher pressure. Three engines were ordered, and delivered in 1926 and being successful, were followed by a further three in 1928.

The engines had bar frames, and cylinders with large piston valves operated by Walschaerts gear. Superheated steam was generated in a large oil-fired boiler with a round-top firebox and Worthington-Simpson feed water heater mounted on the left-hand boiler frame.

The six engines ran until 1959 when they were replaced by diesels, while the railway, following amalgamation with the Northern Longitudinal Railway, is now entitled the Ferrocarril de Iquique a Pueblo Hundido.

Building data are:

FCS Nos	Beyer Peacock Nos	Date
120-22	6291-93	1926
123-25	6481-83	1928

94

Ecuador

Guayaquil and Quito Railway

Although the railways are nationalised into the Empresa de los Ferrocarriles del Estado Ecuatoriano, the Guayaquil and Quito retains its original name, and is the principal railway in the country. One of the most difficult Andean railways, it was built to 3ft 6in gauge by American enterprise, and even today retains much of its American character. Guayaquil itself, the country's main port, is only reached by a rail ferry across the Rio Guayas, and the railway actually starts from Duran, on the east bank. After crossing the coastal flats, the main climb commences at Bucay, 87·4km from Duran, and 294m altitude. By Palmira, 168·9km from Duran, altitude is 3239m, having climbed 2945m (9660ft), in only 81·5km (50·8 miles) on an average gradient of 1 in 28, with maxima of 1 in 18 uncompensated, equalling 1 in 15. Further undulations brought the line to a summit of 3609m (11,841ft) at Urbina, after which it remained at high altitude to the capital city of Quito. During the main climb, between Sibambe and Alausi, the line climbs a precipitous mountain called the Devil's Nose (*Nariz del Diablo*) by means of a zig zag reversing section.

Motive power for this amazing railway has mainly been a series of chunky 2—8—0 tender engines, but with only half the total weight available for adhesion, each has over 50 tons of deadweight which, on these severe gradients, limits hauling capacity to about 100 tons. The American solution was firstly a pair of Shays, built in 1901, followed by two Baldwin 0—6—6—0 Mallets in 1905. Presumably these were not fully satisfactory, for in 1929 Beyer Peacock were able to persuade this otherwise fully American railway to try three Garratts. The dimensions of the Shay and Mallet competitors are unknown to the author, but the comparison between the Garratt and the standard 2—8—0 makes the former very impressive:

Locomotive	2-8-0 + tender	2-6-2 + 2-6-2 Garratt
total weight (lb)	260200	269920
adhesion weight (lb)	131600	181440
tractive effort @ 85% (lb)	32150	42990
resistance on 1 in 18 grade	15150	15720
Nett TE (lb)	17000	27270
increase	—	60,4%

The increase of 60 per cent real haulage capacity for very little extra locomotive weight must have been very attractive for the G & Q, but the extra capacity of the Garratts only just beat the depression, when the railway's tonnage fell from 164,000 in 1928/29, to 116,000 in 1932. Although tonnage was subsequently to increase again, no further articulateds of any type were purchased until eventually diesels were introduced. Further steam locomotives of the 2—8—0 type were supplied until 1953, and judging by the number of passing loops and turntables, there must have been numerous short trains at the peak of traffic, each with two or more locomotives. Larger eight-coupled, Garratts would have made for much more economical working.

The three Garratts built were bar framed jobs with piston valve cylinders and Walschaerts gear, and Worthington feed water heaters. As built, they had Belpaire fireboxes, but a photograph in Obregon's book shows one *reconstruida* with a round topped boiler. How many were so rebuilt is unknown, as is the date taken out of service, probably during the 1960s. The Garratts were G & Q Nos 101—03, Beyer Peacock 6527—29 of 1929. In later days one, or all, had names.

Peru

Central of Peru Railway (FCC)

While the FCAB reaches the highest altitude of any railway in the world, the FCC is the highest standard-gauge line, being only a few feet less, with a maximum of 15,806ft.

The author does not propose to attempt to describe this fascinating line which is covered fully in Brian Fawcett's book *Railways of the Andes*.

Suffice to say, that to tackle its 1 in 22 uncompensated gradients, Cyril Williams sold the railway some large and powerful 2—8—2 + 2—8—2 Garratts, three of which were supplied in 1930, plus one in 1932. These extremely powerful, bar-framed engines were capable of hauling twice the load of the standard 2—8—0 engine, but this proved rather an embarrassment as such loads were too long for the spurs on the zig-zag reversing stations, which meant breaking up and shunting the trains at each reversal. Hence, no further Garratts were purchased but work was found for them until dieselisation, and in 1966 they were stored at Chosica, having by then acquired a large diameter stove-pipe chimney in place of the usual Beyer Peacock type, and no doubt a multiple jet blastpipe had been fitted.

Numbering data were:

First Nos	Second Nos	Beyer Peacock Nos	Date
122-24	400-02	6626-28	1930
125	403	6731	1932

*Central Railway of Peru; two Garratts, with altered
exhaust, stored out of service at Chosica in 1966.*
Howard S. Patrick

*A very rare beast — Columbian Pacific Railway
outside framed 4—6—0 + 0—6—4 Garratt.*   Armstrong
Whitworth

*FC Dorado, Colombia, had two double-Pacific
Garratts on its 3ft gauge railway.*   Beyer Peacock

Class / Type	Cylinders Dia × Stroke (in)	Coupled Wheel Dia (ft in)	Boiler Press (psi)	Tractive Effort @75% (lb)	Grate Area (sq ft)	Max Boiler Dia (ft in)	Heating Surface (sq ft) Fire-box	Tubes	Super-heater	Weights in Working Order (Tons) Max Axle	Ad-hesive	Total	Water Cpcty (Gal)	Fuel Cpcty (Tons/Gal)	Literature Reference	Remarks
Buenos Aires Pacific																
4-8-2- + 2-8-4	18½×26	5-0	200	44490	49·4		281	2161	516	14·13	113·0	194·0	5000	10t		
Buenos Aires Great Southern																
4-8-2 + 2-8-4	17½×26	4-7½	200	43050	44·2		204	2003	442	12·7	101·6	165·6	4600	8t	L192/29	
Cordoba Central																
4-8-2 + 2-8-4	18×26	4-0	185	48700	54·9		213	2202	593	13·1	104·0	168·0	5200	8t		
Entre Rios & North Eastern																
4-4-2 + 2-4-4	15×22	4-8	180	25190	34·4		172	1315	270	12·0	48·0	106·0	3500	5t	L392/27 G856/25	
2-6-0 + 0-6-2	15×22	3-9	180	29700	34·4		172	1315	270	11·75	69·8	90·5	2000	3t	L147/26	
Midland of Buenos Aires																
4-6-2 + 2-6-4	15½×22	4-0	185	30550	34·0		152	1546	335	10·5	63·0	113·3	3600	5t		
Transandine																
2-6-2 + 2-6-2	15×22	3-6	180	31820	39·3		163	1686	334	11·2	66·5	104·5	3000	5t	W207	
Great Western of Brazil																
2-6-2 + 2-6-2	14½×20	3-6	200	30000	28·1	5-8½	121	1196	285	10·2	60·8	89·0	3560	4t		
4-8-2 + 2-8-4	16×24	4-0	200	38400	48·75	6-0	167	1779	370	10·8	84·6	147·4	4200	1500G		
Mogyana																
4-6-0 + 0-6-4	13×20	3-9	180	20280	27·3	(Ins) 4-10⅞	125·2	1422	Nil		51·0	74·1	2000	4t	W201	
4-6-0 + 0-6-4	14×20	3-9	160	20900	27·3	(Ins) 4-10⅞	126	1142	268	8·9	53·3	75·8	2000	4t	W201	
Leopoldina																
2-4-2 + 2-4-2	11×20	3-4	175	15880	30·3		128	793	182	8·9	34·6	68·9	1700	2·5t	G588/43 G74/46	
4-6-2 + 2-6-4	15½×22	4-2	185	29330	34·0		151	1546	335	10·5	63·0	111·5	3500	4·5t	G856/25	
São Paulo																
2-6-0 + 0-6-2	14×20	3-6	200	28000	29·8		139	1726	Nil	10·5	62·7	80·8	3000	9t	L151/16 G61/28	
2-4-0 + 0-4-2	16×24	5-0	160	24580	30·0	5-6	145	1396	304	13·95	55·7	80·5	1500	700G		
2-6-2 + 2-6-2	20×26	5-6	200	47270	49·2	6-9	205	2749	668	18·5	111·0	158·25	3100	5t	L21/28	
4-6-2 + 2-6-4	20×26	5-6	200	47270	49·2	6-9	205	2749	668	19·3	115·8	191·25	4000	5t	L173/35	
Rio Grande do Sul																
4-6-2 + 2-6-4	14×24	3-9	199	31300	43·2	4-11½	163·5	1178	478		56·8	112·1	17m³	11·2t	H32/32 H14/32	2 syphons
Antofagasta (Chile) & Bolivia																
4-8-2 + 2-8-4	18×26	4-0	185	48700	54·9	6-9	217	2647	593	13·0	104·0	169·5	5000	1670G	L241/29	
4-8-2 + 2-8-4	18×26	4-0	185	48700	54·9	6-9	217	2647	546	14·5	116·0	181·75	5500	2200G	G179/51	
Nitrate Railways																
2-8-2 + 2-8-2	22×20	3-6	200	69150	68·8	7-3½	276	3070	744	18·0	141·5	187·15	5500	1410G	RE242/26 L171/26	
Guayaquil & Quito																
2-6-2 + 2-6-2	15½×20	3-2	200	37930	40·4		171	1784	383	13·5	81·0	120·5	2500	2500G	L191/29	
Pacifico																
4-6-0 + 0-6-4	16×22	3-4			34·8		156	1814	300	10·0	63·45	96·0	2650	7t	W201	
Dorada																
4-6-2 + 2-6-4	14×22	3-4	180	29110	39·0		175	1400	270	10·0	59·9	117·6	3500	1500G	L377/37	
Central Peru																
2-8-2 + 2-8-2	19½×22	3-9	205	57160	61·25	7-3½	244	2598	678	16·0	128·0	173·5	5050	4½t	L262/30	

Colombia

The Colombian National Railways, Ferrocarriles Nacionales de Colombia, operates an extensive system of 3ft 0in gauge, gradually taken over from private concerns. Articulated power has been used to a considerable extent, the most popular type being the Kitson-Meyer. In fact, the last Kitson-Meyers ever built, and probably the finest, were the 2—8—8—2Ts built by Robert Stephenson & Co in 1935. Another curious type, introduced the previous year, was an 0—6—6—0T with a water-tube boiler and Sentinel geared units which, with a somewhat bulbous curved casing, looked rather like a pregnant hippopotamus!

However, the Garratt was represented by two classes, the first being a pair of 4—6—0 + 0—6—4 built by Armstrong Whitworth for the Ferrocarril Pacifico de Colombia. These unusual-looking engines had outside plate frames and slightly inclined piston-valve cylinders. The outside cranks had integral balance weights, while return cranks drove the Walschaerts gear. Belpaire boilers were mounted, and they were superheated.

The other Garratt class also comprised two locomotives only, and these were 4—6—2 + 2—6—4s designed and built by Beyer Peacock, for the F.C. Dorada.

In this case the frames were of the bar type, and inside the wheels, while the boiler was of the round-top type, and fitted with thermic syphons in the firebox. These Dorada engines were heavier than the Pacifico engines but had less tractive effort, although designed to haul 350 ton trains over the 1 in 50 gradients between Honda and Marequita. All are now scrapped.

Building data are:

Railway	Type	Running Nos	Builder	Builders' Nos	Date
F.C. Pacifico	4-6-0- + 0-6-4	29-30	Armstrong Whitworth	565-66	1924
F.C. Dorada	4-6-2 + 2-6-4	17-18	Beyer Peacock	6843-44	1938

Chapter 7

Africa

The main Garratt-using railways in Africa are covered by the following three chapters, and within this one are the Garratt details of North Africa, West Africa, and the offshore islands.

NORTH AFRICA

Algeria

Algerian railways were among the first users of Garratt locomotives and, at a much later date, users of some of the finest, and certainly the fastest and the most striking-looking Garratts ever built.

Société Anonyme des Mines du Zaccar

One of the earliest users of Garratt locomotives, the Zaccar mines railway was sufficiently obscure that there remain a few details requiring confirmation. Feeding onto the main line not far from Algiers, some enthusiasts must have seen the little Garratts without, apparently, anybody having photographed them in service. Even exact details of what was mined there have so far eluded the author, while there are two gauge variations recorded: Lartilleux's geographical book quotes 600mm, but the builder's catalogue shows 750mm. One assumes that the builder knew what he built, and as this is a more original source, it will be assumed until proved otherwise that the railway and its Garratts were 750mm gauge.

Zaccar was an area rather than a place; the Djebel du Zaccar was a ridge of the Atlas mountains, south of which was the Forêt du Zaccar, in which was the mine, close to the town or village of Miliana. The railway connected the mine with the station of Miliana-Margueritte, between Blida and Orleansville, about 100km west of Algiers. The mine line itself was about 10km long, rather short considering the number of locomotives which appear to have been used. The first Garratt, by St Léonard, was similar to those supplied just previously to the CF Mayumbe in the Belgian Congo, and was an outside framed 0—4—0 + 0—4—0. Whether or not the later engines, from a different builder, were from the same drawings the author has been unable to ascertain, although it is likely that small detail variations occurred. Building details were:

Zaccar Nos	Name	Builder	Builders' Nos	Date
5	*Marguerite*	St Léonard	1781	1912
8	*Adelia*	Haine St Pierre	1752	1936
9	*Pierre Noire*	Haine St Pierre	1783	1937

Société Anonyme des Mines du Zaccar, Algeria, No 5 Marguerite, *a miniscule 0—4—0 + 0—4—0 Garratt built in 1912.* Société St Léonard

A French built Garratt, No 241-142 YAT-2 of the Algerian Railways 1.050m gauge section, in 1952.
H. Pearce

PLM Algeria

The main railways in Algeria were, until just before World War II, owned and operated by that great French institution, the Chemins de Fer Paris á Lyon et á la Méditerranée, and for their 1055mm-gauge line inland from Blidah, near Algiers, to Djelfa at the foot of the Atlas mountains, the Société Franco-Belge at Raismes supplied in 1931 four 4—8—2 + 2—8—4 Garratts based upon the Kenya Uganda Railways EC1 class. Built under licence from Beyer Peacock, these engines differed in appearance quite considerably in having tanks rounded at all corners, three large headlights, a stove-pipe chimney, ACFI feedwater heater, and the pumps and air reservoirs associated with air brakes. The cabside had central doors with a window each side, while the couplings were of the buckeye type.

In service, they hauled 360 ton trains up gradients of 1 in 40 at 10mph, and by 1934 it was computed that they were saving 17 per cent of fuel compared with the conventional locomotives previously used. At some later stage, the single large chimney was replaced by a double chimney placed across the smokebox, an unusual arrange-

ment peculiar to Algerian Garratts and dictated by the proportions of the short, fat smokebox. These engines were in service until the early 1960s, when the line was fully dieselised.

The year after, Franco-Belge supplied a prototype 4—6—2 + 2—6—4 express Garratt for the 4ft 8½in-gauge main line section, between Algiers and Oran, which has gradients as steep as 1 in 38½ on which 2—10—2T banking engines were employed, and yet had long stretches with easy gradients where high speeds could be attained. To avoid the necessity of banking the express trains, the use of a Garratt was proposed, and a memorable design evolved in collaboration with Beyer Peacock.

There was nothing new, of course, about an express Garratt, for in 1927 Beyer Peacock had built six 2—6—2 + 2—6—2s with 5ft 6in wheels for the São Paulo Railway in Brazil, these being soon converted to double Pacifics. Then, in 1931, Euskalduña supplied the six 4—6—2 + 2—6—4s with 5ft 9in wheels to the Central of Aragon Railway. A further and final increase in wheel diameter to nearly 5ft 11in was reached with the Algerian engine.

Apart from its large dimensions, the only

The original Algerian express Garratt, as built to the order of the PLM.   La Vie du Rail

unusual feature of the locomotive was the inclusion of Beyer Peacock's rotary bunker, the engine being hand fired. Plate frames were used and piston-valve cylinders, together with Walschaerts valve gear. The Belpaire boiler had an ACFI feedwater heater, and single 'Kylchap' exhaust, while the tanks and cab were of similar design to those of the narrow-gauge Garratts.

Upon completion, the engine was tried out on the PLM main line between Laroche and Dijon, twenty-six 'Rapide' trains being hauled over this section, plus freight and stopping trains. A test with train No 610 was particularly satisfactory, since a load of 558 tonnes was hauled up the seventeen miles of 1 in 125 gradient to Blaisy Bas summit at an average speed of 38mph, including a check to 20mph, while a maximum down-grade speed of 75mph was attained, then a record for an articulated locomotive.

The engine was then shipped to Algeria where it acquitted itself well, although found not to have quite as much power as was needed to cope with the loads offering. Hence, in 1935, it was fitted with new cylinders, Cossart valves and valve gear, a double 'Kylchap' chimney placed transversely, and smoke deflectors, these latter being mounted on both the front tank and the smokebox side.

While these modifications increased the output, it was felt that for the production batch a yet more powerful type was required, and tenders were called for further Garratts.

Among the proposals received was an extremely interesting design by Henschel for a 4—6—2 + 2—6—4 with four-cylinder compound propulsion on each unit, eight cylinders in all. To feed these, an immense boiler was proposed, 2500mm (8ft 2½in) maximum diameter, and tapered, while the firebox, which included a combustion chamber and thermic syphons, had 8sq metres (86sq ft) of grate area. Fuel only was to be carried on the engine, fed to the firebox by a mechanical stoker, water being carried in an auxiliary tender, in the manner later adopted by South Africa. The engine was rather over-designed for the job, which called for the haulage of 400 ton trains up 2·3 per cent gradients at 55kph, a performance which calls for about 3500 to 4000 indicated horsepower, whereas the Henschel design was clearly capable of an extra thousand ihp over and above that required.

It is hardly surprising, therefore, that the design chosen was a straightforward enlargement of the prototype Garratt, the new engines having increased grate area and boiler pressure, and were rated at 3200 *cheval*, or metric horsepower. A technical development of interest was the use of an electric servomotor to operate the reverse gear, and the rotary bunker was replaced by a fixed bunker, having top hatches for closure, plus

One of the amazing streamlined Algerian express Garratts, with Cossart valve gear, shown here at the head of a Paris express at Calais Maritime station, while on test. Author's collection

a coal pusher, the engines remaining hand fired, two firemen being employed. The transverse double chimneys were fitted from the start while a larger superheater was included. Mechanical stokers were later fitted.

The really striking feature of the engine was the styling, both the front tank and the rear tank and bunker being cylindrical, and of the same diameter and on the same centre line as the boiler. Each end was streamlined, while smoke deflector plates were also incorporated, matching a 'skyline' boiler casing.

One of the new engines, No 231−132.BT.11, was tried out on the main line from Paris Nord to Calais and attained a maximum speed of 82mph, while an output of 3000dbhp was reached on the climb to Survilliers summit.

In service, they ran over the whole length of the Algerian main line from the Tunisian border at Ghardimaou to the Moroccan frontier of Oudja, a distance of 850 miles. Speeds of up to 75mph were scheduled in an average, over 171 miles, of 60mph with 67 miles at 65mph, the loads being 466 tons.

Unfortunately, these express Garratts had a very short life, being largely run down during the war, and replaced by diesels almost immediately afterwards, the whole class being out of service by 1951. Incidentally, the streamlined Garratts were delivered to the Algerian State Railways (Chemins de Fer Algeriens) who had taken over the railways from the PLM.

Building data are:

Engine Nos	Gauge	Type	Franco-Belge Nos	Date
241-142-YAT.1-4	1050mm	4-8-2 + 2-8-4	2673-76	1931
231-132.AT.-1	Standard	4-6-2 + 2-6-4	2678	1932
231-132.BT.1-12	,,	,,	2697-708	1936
231-132.BT.13-16	,,	,,	2711-14	1937
231-132.BT.17-22	,,	,,	2725-30	1939
231-132.BT.23-29	,,	,,	2741-47	1940

Sudan

The Sudan Railways had but one class of Garratt, and ran them only for a short time, but they were of a hitherto unused wheel arrangement and became a much-travelled group of locomotives, still being used today by their third owners.

With much of the track as light as 50lb per yd, the problems involved were to obtain a reasonably high tractive effort and large water capacity without overstressing the track, problems for which the Garratt is an obvious solution.

The 4−6−4 + 4−6−4 type was chosen, the engines having bar frames, Walschaerts-actuated piston valves and a Belpaire firebox with arch tubes. The original duties included the line from Port Sudan to Atbara, which included sixteen miles of 1 in 100 on 50lb track, and also Atbara to Wad Medani, the portion from Khartoum being over 50lb track.

The onset of dieselisation after the war, plus the laying of heavier track capable of supporting a 4−8−2, made these engines redundant after only twelve years' service, and they were sold in 1949 to the Rhodesian Railways who ran them for fifteen years, before selling them again to

Double Baltic Garratt No 252 of the Sudan Railways.
These inspired the better known Rhodesian 15th
class, and were later bought by RR.   Beyer Peacock

Only six Garratts were built in Italy, one of which is
shown here in Ethiopia, the country for which they
were designed by Ansaldo.   C. S. Small

Developed from the Algerian narrow gauge Garratts were the West African version, represented here by 93.225 of the Abidjan-Niger railway, Ivory Coast.
La Vie du Rail

Mozambique, where they are still at work. Building data were:

SR Nos	Beyer Peacock Nos	Date	RR Nos	CFM Nos
250-253	6798-6801	1936	271-4	921-4
254-259	6870-6875	1937	275-80	925-30

Ethiopia

Chemins de Fer Franco-Ethiopien

This line, which runs from Djibouti in French Somaliland to Addis Ababa in Ethiopia, is described well in C. S. Small's book *Far Wheels*. Climbing from the coast, it reaches an altitude of 7704ft at its terminus and was run mainly with 2—8—0s. However, after the Italian conquest, it was decided to use Garratts and six were built by Ansaldo in 1939. Of these only the first three reached Djibouti, as late as 1943—4, and were put to work after the war. The other three were shipped to Tripoli, having been presumably converted from their original metre to 950mm gauge. Of these three, one never arrived, and is no doubt now lying at the bottom of the Mediterranean after being torpedoed, while the other two were so badly damaged by bombing that they were scrapped in 1945. How they performed, when they ran at all, seems not on record, but they were presumably as 'woolly' as other Italian steam locomotives. Even a full set of dimensions seems not available, as Ansaldo, who built them, and who had been building steam locomotives since 1854, have now convinced themselves that steam is 'dead' to such an extent that they deny having ever built such a machine!

Building data are:

CFE Nos	Ansaldo Nos	Date	Notes
501-503	1371-73	1939	Withdrawn by 1959
504-506	1374-76	1939	To Tripoli

Senegal and Ivory Coast

These French colonies shared a railway administration known as the Regie des Chemins de fer de l'Afrique Occidentale Francaise and no less than twenty-seven 4—8—2 + 2—8—4 Garratts were supplied to the administration from 1938 to 1941. Built by Franco-Belge, they were used on the Dakar-Niger line in Senegal and the Abijan to Bobo Dioulasso railway running from the Ivory Coast Atlantic shores into the neighbouring territory now called Upper Volta, once all part of French West Africa.

Senegal had two of the first and the whole of the final batch, to start with, but eventually all were transferred to the Ivory Coast. Like the Algerian express Garratts, they had a short life, the railways being dieselised in the late 1950s, while being of metre gauge there was no ready market for them.

Handsome engines, they were noticeably from the same stable as the streamlined Algerian Garratts, but had ordinary piston-valve cylinders and Walschaerts valve gear in place of the Cossart motion. Tanks and bunker had a semi-circular bottom and rectangular top with rounded corners, together with smoke deflectors. The Belpaire boilers had double chimneys, mounted transversely, and a skyline casing.

Despite their small wheels, speeds up to 62mph were attained on trial, although their main use was in freight work, 400 ton loads being hauled on 1 in 40 gradients. The fuel burned was local hardwood, and the numbering system used commenced with the adhesion weight in metric tons.

Building data were:

Railway Nos	Franco-Belge Nos	Date
93.201-210	2715-24	1938
93.211-220	2731-40	1939
93.221-227	2748-54	1941

Sierra Leone

Sierra Leone Government Railways

This 2ft 6in-gauge system was a fairly early user of Garratts, the first being built for them in 1926. These were 2—6—2 + 2—6—2, equal capacity to the previous 2—6—2T plus 4—8—0 which had previously double-headed the trains. A maximum axle load of only 5 tons was permissible on the

South Africa *Sowing the seeds of its own destruction, an SAR GCA heads a work train, laying heavier rails to enable branch line diesels to replace the diminutive Garratt on the Underberg line.*
A. E. Durrant

(above)   The 1 in 30 gradients of the Eshowe branch needed Garratts to cope with long trains of empties to load sugar cane. Quixotically, the daily milk and school train, downhill, used the power available on the line — a GEA 4–8–2 + 2–8–4 on two coaches!
A. E. Durrant

(below)   The small front tank of a GM emphasised the boiler diameter. One of three returned to service after withdrawal, No 2304 is seen near Ermelo, running cab-first, as normal with this class.
A. E. Durrant

One of the original Garratts on the Sierra Leone Government Railways designed to double the capacity of the 2—6—2T engines formerly used.
Beyer Peacock

30lb track, while 1 in 50 gradients and 5 chain curves had to be negotiated on the main line, which is no less than 227 miles long. Of this, the first 22 miles from Freetown inland are the most difficult, and include a steeply graded section where Garratts and banked trains run through the streets!

The first Garratt design was a little job with inside plate frames and piston valves actuated by Walschaerts gear. The boiler was superheated with a Belpaire firebox and burned coal, these features being maintained on all subsequent Garratts. Front tanks had rounded top corners, but the rear tank/bunker was 'all-square'.

Three engines of the original design were supplied and, proving highly satisfactory, repeat orders continued for seventeen years until there were thirteen engines. During the war five of them were converted to 2—8—0 + 0—8—2 in order

to increase the adhesion weight, which was not really adequate when working hard with empty tanks, the adhesion factor under these conditions dropping to 3·5.

After the war, traffic developing, a large order was placed for no less than fourteen new Garratts of an entirely new 4—8—2 + 2—8—4 type. These included the same basic technical features as the smaller engines, but the cylinders were of modern design, tanks and bunkers of 'streamlined' contours, while roller bearings were used on the carrying axles, the inner two-wheel trucks having outside bearings.

A massive increase was represented by these small yet modern locomotives, which were painted green and proved to be the last new steam acquired for the railway. Despite dieselisation, which increasingly showed itself unreliable, steam was retained until the railway's closure in

The final Sierra Leone Garratts — quite big engines on a little gauge, although the smallest eight-coupled Garratts ever built. Beyer Peacock

1976, by which time about half the surviving traffic was steam worked. Unfortunately, by the time many people realised what had happened, most of the locomotives, including all the Garratts, had been shipped off to Japan for scrap, although a 2—6—2T and some coaches have been preserved on the Welshpool & Llanfair Railway in Wales.

Details of building dates and numbers, etc are tabulated below:

SLGR Nos	Type	Beyer Peacock Nos	Date
50-52*	2-6-2 + 2-6-2*	6297-99	1926
53-54*	,,	6497-98	1928
55-56*	,,	6578-79	1929
57-60	,,	7045-48	1942
61-62	,,	7049-50	1943
63-76	4-8-2 + 2-8-4	7707-20	1955-56

*Nos 52-56 converted to 2-8-0 + 0-8-2.

Sierra Leone Development Co

This railway, unlike the Government railways, is of 3ft 6in gauge and is purely a mineral line, for the conveyance of iron ore to the port of Pepel from the workings at Marampa, 52½ miles inland. Well engineered gradients against the load were kept to a maximum of 1 in 125 and with 65lb track an axle load of 13 tons was permitted.

Opened in 1931, the line commenced operations with two 2—8—2 + 2—8—2 Garratts of the same design as South Africa's GE class. Two more were supplied later and these sufficed until the late 1950s when the line was dieselised. Apart from shunting tanks, these Garratts handled all the traffic in steam days, this being the only railway in the world where all traffic between inception to the end of steam was hauled by Garratts.

Upon dieselisation, the Garratts were offered for sale but, finding no buyers, were scrapped. Details were:

Nigerian Railways double Pacific Garratt No 502, Emir Katsina. Beyer Peacock

SLDC Nos	Beyer Peacock Nos	Date
3-4	6726-27	1931
5	6786	1936
6	6842	1937

Ghana

Ghana Railways (formerly Gold Coast Railway)

This extensive 3ft 6in-gauge system, running inland from the ports of Takoradi and Accra to Kumasi, was not a great Garratt user, and its only six were of the wartime 2—8—2 + 2—8—2 type, delivered for hauling heavy manganese traffic needed as war material. As Ghana Railways Nos 301—306, they were withdrawn from service on 30 June 1960. Buildings details are given in Chapter 11.

Sierra Leone Development Corporation. One of the Garratts built to the design of South African Railways GE class (second series). Beyer Peacock

Nigeria

Another West Coast railway of 3ft 6in gauge. Nigeria also had some very light track, this time only 45lb/yd, limiting axle loads to 9½ tons. These sections were up country, from Jebba to Minna and Zaria to Kano, while heavy rails of 80lb section were used on the main line from Lagos. It being desirable to run the same loads right through for operating convenience, an articulated type was necessary to avoid double-heading, and the Garratt was naturally chosen.

The first excursion into the Garratt concept consisted of two 4—8—2 + 2—8—4s which were the largest engines ever built for 45lb rail, and these were of conventional construction having plate frames, piston valves, Walschaerts gear and superheated Belpaire boilers. In service they proved rather more powerful than was convenient, being capable of hauling greater loads over the light track than the three-cylinder 4—8—2s could manage on the 80lb rails.

Accordingly, further Garratts were of a smaller 4—6—2 + 2—6—4 design of comparable power to the 4—8—2s, and this enabled through trains to be run, changing only engines and not remarshalling to suit the engine power.

Of the Pacific Garratts, the first two had a relatively high pressure with smaller cylinders than the remainder, the general design features being as on the earlier 4—8—2 + 2—8—4 Garratts. At one stage a three-cylinder 2—10—4 was considered for this light track, but it is interesting to note that the Garratt was eventually preferred.

All the Nigerian Garratts were painted Midland Red and looked particularly fine in this livery, while names were carried as shown below:

NR Nos	Names	Beyer Peacock Nos	Date
201 (later 901)	*Emir of Kano*	6635	1930
202 (later 902)	*Emir of Zania*	6636	1930
501	*Sultan of Sokoto**	6781	1935
502	*Emir of Katsina**	6782	1935
503	*Shehu of Bornu**	6783	1935
504	*Emir of Gwandu**	6784	1935
505	*Emir of Gwandu*	6796	1936
506	*Emir of Bauchi*	6797	1936
507	*Emir of Argungu*	6861	1937
508	*Emir of Bida*	6862	1937
509	*Lamido of Adamawa*	6863	1937
510	*Emir of Kontagorra*	6864	1937
511	*Shehu of Dikwa*	6865	1937
512	*Emir of Hadejia*	6866	1937
513	*Sir John Maybin*	6927	1939
514	*Sir William Hunt*	6928	1939
515	*M. P. Sells*	6929	1939
516	*Sir John Maybin*	6930	1939
517	*Sir Aubrey Graham*	7051	1943
518	*Emir of Bauchi*	7052	1943
519	*Sultan of Sokoto*	7053	1943
520	*G. V. O. Bulkeley*	7054	1943
521	*Shehu of Bornu*	7055	1943
522	*Emir of Gwanda*	7056	1943

***Later:**
501	*Sir Bernard Bourdillon*		
502	*Sultan of Sokoto*		
503	*Emir of Katsina*		
504	*Shehu of Bornu*		

Note: as earlier locomotives were scrapped, names were transferred to later ones.

By the end of the 1970s there were more diesels in Nigeria than steam locomotives and there were also plans for replacement by 4ft 8½in gauge lines.

Congo

Chemins de Fer Congo Ocean

This French-owned railway, from Pointe Noire to

Mauritius Railways 2—8—0 + 0—8—2 Garratt, three of which were auctioned for scrap following the railway's closure. Beyer Peacock

Brazzaville was, during the war, allocated three of the British War Department 2—8—2 + 2—8—2 Garratts, details of which are in Chapter 11. Following the dieselisation of this line in the 1950s, the three engines were sold to the Moçambique railways, where they are still at work.

Offshore Islands

Malagasy Republic (formerly Madagascar)

This is the largest island in the world, and lies off the coast of Mozambique. Formerly a French possession, the metre-gauge railway on the island was noted for its reliance on 0—4—4—0 Mallet tank engines with four-wheel tenders.

However, in 1926, St Léonard supplied a pair of 2—6—0 + 0—6—2 wood-burning Garratts, the largest and most powerful engines to run on the island. These had inside plate frames, and piston valves actuated by Walschaerts gear. The boiler was of the Belpaire type and had an outside steam pipe from the dome to the superheater header, and further outside pipes from the header down the sides of the smokebox, carrying the superheated steam. The ensemble was completed by a diamond type spark-arresting chimney, one of the few Garratt classes to sport such a 'Wild West' appurtenance.

The Malagasy railways are now fully dieselised but the two Garratts, St Léonard numbers 2031—

2032 of 1926, are still believed to be rusting away. Originally numbered simply 101—2, their later railway numbers were 59—801—2.

Mauritius (Ile Maurice)

A small British island off the coast of Madagascar, Mauritius possessed a railway system surprisingly of 4ft 8½in gauge, and comprising sixty-eight miles of route. The motive power comprised some curious specimens such as a Kitson-built 0—8—0T with inside cylinders, and for working the Port St Louis to Mahebourg line, which climbed to the summit at Curepipe by means of 1 in 26 and 1 in 27 gradients, Beyer Peacock supplied, in 1927, three 2—8—0 + 0—8—2 Garratts.

These were very powerful machines for their size and had plate frames with piston-valve cylinders, Walschaerts valve gear and a super-heated Belpaire boiler. They arrived at a season of maximum traffic, since when the railways have slowly declined, passenger traffic ceasing in 1956 and the railways closing completely in 1964. During the latter years of operation traffic was never sufficiently heavy to employ the Garratts which, with the other locomotives, were offered for sale by auction in 1967, and were presumably bought for scrap. In their heyday, the Garratts could haul a load of 350 tons on a 1 in 25 gradient, and were numbered 60—62; the Beyer Peacock numbers were 6381—6383 of 1927.

*(below) Belgian-built 2—6—0 + 0—6—2 of the
Madagascar Railways, wood burning, and with spark
arresting chimney.   C. S. Small*

AFRICA (GENERAL)

Class	Type	Cylinders Dia × Stroke (in)	Coupled Wheel Dia (ft in)	Boiler Press (psi)	Tractive Effort @ 75% (lb)	Grate Area sq ft	Max Boiler Dia (Outs) ft in	Heating Surface (sq ft) Fire-box	Tubes	Super-heater	Weights in Working Order (Tons) Max Axle	Ad-hesive	Total	Water Cpcty (Gal)	Fuel Cpcty (Tons /Gal)	Literature Reference
Zaccar Mines																
	0-4-0 + 0-4-0	9×13·78	2-2⅜	178	12945	15·3	3-9¼	60·2	579·5	Nil	7·0	27·5	27·5	744	1t	
Algerian State Railways																L97/32
AT	4-6-2 + 2-6-4	19·3×26	5-10⅞	227	47300	54·6	6-10¾	236·8	2852·5	742·7	17·0	102·0	192·0	5500	6·9t	L268/32
BT	4-6-2 + 2-6-4	19·3×26	5-10⅞	284	58200	58·1	6-10¾	220	2574	975	18·2	109·2	212·6	6600	10·8t	L109/36
YAT	4-8-2 + 2-8-4	16½×22	3-7	200	41790	43·6		174	1863	385	11·3	86·8	142	6270	6t	L44/32
Sudan																G375/37
250	4-6-4 + 4-6-4	16¾×26	4-9	200	38400	43·2	6-0	184	1776	440	12·5	74·6	168·8	7000	10t	L101/37
Ethiopia																
	2-8-2 + 2-8-2	14·95×21·6	3-11¼	198	34900								86·6			
Senegal and Ivory Coast															Wood	
93	4-8-2 + 2-8-4	17×24	4-3	200	40800	47·0	6-0	186	1805	258	11·5	92	148	6160	5·9t	L151/39
Sierra Leone Government																
	2-6-2 + 2-6-2	10×16	2-4	175	15000	18·2		76·5	647·5	120·0	5·0	30	46·7	1200	3t	L311/26
	2-8-0 + 0-8-2	10×16	2-4	200	17125	18·2		76·5	647·5	120·0	5·0			1200	3t	
	4-8-2 + 2-8-4	12⅝×16	2-9	175	20290	22·5		95	829	178	5·0	40	66·3	1600	4t	L60/56
Sierra Leone Development Co																
	2-8-2 + 2-8-2	18×24	3-9½	180	46140	51·5	6-9	224	2366	34·4	13·0	103·6	151	4600	9t	
Gold Coast, also Congo Ocean Rly																
	2-8-2 + 2-8-2	19×24	3-9½	180	51410	51·3	7-0	212	2328	470	13·1	104	151·8	4600	9t	G273/45
Nigeria																
501	4-6-2 + 2-6-4	13½×26	4-0	200	29610	31·4	5-4½	154	1363	333	9·75	58·4	111·5	3240	7t	L32/36
901	4-8-2 + 2-8-4	16½×23	4-0	180	35220	38·8	6-0	163	1605	368	9·5	76	125·8	3800	5t	L98/31
Madagascar															Wood	
	2-6-0 + 0-6-2	14¼×19¾	3-3¾	170	29600	24·21		114·5	1090·6	258·3	10	59	72·5	1100	353ft³	L177/26
Mauritius																L205/27
60	2-8-0 + 0-8-2	19×24	3-10¼	200	55890	53·9	6-6	213·5	2266	522·5	16·16	127·5	155	5000	6t	—

Chapter 8

South Africa

SAR 3ft 6in Gauge

The railways of South Africa were among the first to become interested in the Garratt type, and were soon to become the largest users of Garratts in the world, a position maintained even in the early 1980s, with about 150 in stock on SAR on two gauges, plus others in industrial service. Ten years earlier, SAR had about 400 Garratts hard at work, undoubtably the largest collection of the type seen anywhere in the world, but today the position is sadly different, with many of the older Garratts scrapped, and the more modern locomotives largely in store, or on loan to other railways in Africa, particularly Zimbabwe and Mozambique.

Geographically, South Africa is similar to Spain, having a large central plateau, bounded south, east, and west by the sea, making the inland routes from the ports and harbours extremely heavily graded and difficult to work. As the South African plateau is generally about a mile above sea level, the continuous hard steaming necessary to bring traffic from the coast can well be imagined. Furthermore, even the inland lines, on gently rolling country, generally follow the lie of the land with the minimum amount of earthworks, so that conditions of almost equal severity occur on these sections also.

The South African Railways and Harbour administration was formed in 1910, at the time of Union of the former territories, from the Natal Government Railways, the Cape Government Railways, and the Central South Africa Railways, plus the inevitable minor lines. One exception was the New Cape Central Railway which remained independent until 1925, the only individual railway other than industrial concerns in the Union to acquire Garratts. The South African Railways, or Suid-Afrikaanse Spoorwëe, is by far the largest railway system on the African continent, and by a close margin beats Japan in having the largest narrow-gauge system in the world. Still growing, the route mileage today is longer than the British Railways' planned 'rationalised' system, while with its virtual monopoly of freight traffic, SAR remains a viable system.

As might be expected, the provision of adequate motive power within the limits of the 3ft 6in gauge became a matter requiring con-tinual development, and South Africa was, in 1909, one of the first countries in the world to adopt the 4—8—2 type which once, in various sizes, was the principal means of motive power, nearly 1400 of these useful engines being in service; even in 1980 over 900 were in stock.

However, for the more heavily graded sections, articulateds became necessary, and the SAR and its constituents have always been willing to explore the possibilities of such power. In fact, from 1875 to the present day, articulateds have always been to hand, from a modest beginning on the Cape Government Railways, with a Fairlie, for the East London to Kingwilliamstown line. This, together with another supplied in 1880, lasted until 1903 when a Kitson-Meyer was experimented with, unsuccessfully. Then, in 1910, the Natal Government Railways intro-duced the Mallet type which was successful, provided that speeds remained low, and eighty-one of this type were eventually built, up to 1921. In an attempt to overcome the sluggishness of the type two interesting experimental loco-motives were placed in service, one, Class ME, being a superheated simple-expansion Mallet, as later adopted extensively in the USA, while the other, Class MG, had larger wheels on the front low-pressure unit than on the rear high-pressure.

These modifications to the basic Mallet concept were, however, insufficient to make it competi-tive with the Garratt type, the first of which were ordered in 1914 although, because of the first world war, delivery was not made until 1919—21. The initial orders comprised three locomotives for the 2ft 0in gauge, and two experimental types for the 3ft 6in-gauge lines. It is proposed here to deal first with all the SAR 3ft 6in-gauge Garratts and then to follow with the 2ft 0in-gauge and finally industrial locomotives.

The first 3ft 6in-gauge locomotive, Class GA, was by far the largest Garratt ever built at the time, and with a 17·8 ton axle load was a thorough main-line engine. The wheel arrangement was 2—6—0 + 0—6—2, and the design was generally up to date, having piston-valve cylinders, although with Z ports and short-lap valves, while piston tail rods were incor-porated. The frames were of plate. The boiler was superheated and had a Belpaire firebox, this being current SAR practice. Valves were provided so that the steam supply to either unit could be shut off at will in case of failure, a

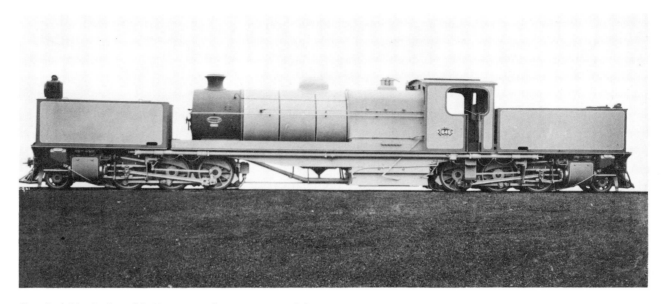

South Africa's first 3ft 6in gauge Garratt, class GA.
Beyer Peacock

feature, now discontinued, which indicated a degree of caution concerning the Garratt type. The engine was tried out on the Natal main line, in competition with an MH Mallet of equivalent tractive effort, and the results came out decidedly in favour of the Garratt, which was able to haul a greater load at higher speeds than the Mallet, and with less consumption of coal and water. These tests were carried out between Estcourt and Stockton Tunnel, just before Dell, and the 14th class 4—8—2 was also tested, although of course, it was unable to handle the loads of the articulateds. The test results were:

Class of Engine	GA	MH	14
Type	2-6-0 + 0-6-2	2-6-6-2	4-8-2
Weight of locomotive (tons)	134	180	140
Tractive effort 75% (lb)	47385	48372	37359
Load hauled (tons)	1011	981	699
Coal per 100 ton-miles (lb)	17·7	21·2	20·4
Water per 100 ton-miles (gal)	13·4	15·9	14·9
Running time (min)	118	137·5	127

It is interesting to note that the superior running speeds of the Garratt were achieved mainly on the downhill sections, the Mallet's brute force equalling the Garratt uphill. This is logical, the Garratt being generally smoother riding and freer running than a compound Mallet. This feature may also have had a bearing upon the relative economies, with perhaps the Mallet needing steam on where the Garratt was able to freewheel.

It is also interesting to compare the boiler dimensions of the Garratt and Mallet, as being of comparable capacity, and showing how the short, fat Garratt boiler, without combustion chamber, weighs empty some 11 tons less than the Mallet equivalent:

Type	Mallet (MH)	Garratt (GA)
Grate area (sq ft)	53·17	51·83
Max dia (inside)	6' 4¼"	6' 9"
Length between tubeplates	22' 0"	11' 8¼"
Firebox volume (cu ft)	327	311
Firebox heating surface (sq ft)	250	211·3
Tube heating surface (sq ft)	2961	2343·2
Superheating surface (sq ft)	616	526·5
Empty weight (tons)	35·5	24·5

The GA spent most of its life in Natal, latterly running passenger trains from Ladysmith to Harrismith, including the climb of 1 in 30 up to Van Reenen's pass. The design was not repeated as the lack of inner carrying wheels led to heavy flange wear, and as an odd engine it was scrapped in 1938, the boiler being retained as a spare for the GE class. Nevertheless, the GA established the Garratt type in South Africa, and served its purpose well.

The second experimental Garratt, Class GB, was only half the size of the GA, being intended for very lightly laid branches, and the maximum axle load was as low as 7·8 tons. The GB was a 2—6—2 + 2—6—2 type and apart from the size and wheel arrangement contained the same technical features as the GA. The first GB was tried out on the South Coast line from Durban, which was then poorly laid, and following its complete success, a further six were ordered and placed in service on the Port Alfred and Barkly East branches in the Cape Province, both of which included compensated gradients of 1 in 30. The GBs put in a long and useful life, ending their days on the Barkly East branch in 1966 while one

Two lightweight locomotives at Queenstown, South Africa, having similar tractive capacities. The GB Garratt has a lower axle load than the 7BS 4—8—0.
A. E. Durrant

is now preserved at Aliwal North. The second batch of GBs differed from the first in having side window cabs.

Having thus established the worth of the Garratt, the CME, Col Collins, prepared specifications for four further types of Garratt of differing size and power, and for different duties. These were:

(a) 2—6—2 + 2—6—2, 10½ ton axle load for branches
(b) 2—6—2 + 2—6—2, 12½ ton axle load for branches
(c) 2—8—2 + 2—8—2, 13   ton axle load for branches
(d) 2—6—2 + 2—6—2, 16   ton axle load for main line passenger

Of these, (a) and (b) were progressive enlargements of the GB, while (c) and (d) were developments of the GA, and in fact utilised the same boiler design.

However, at this stage the North British Locomotive Company, who had supplied a large number of locomotives to South Africa, became alarmed at the thought of losing business to Beyer Peacock, who owned the patent rights in the Garratt, and set about evolving an alternative type of articulated for consideration.

The result was a modified Kitson-Meyer with the side tanks removed to the front so that it looked rather like a Garratt, but both front and rear tanks were cantilevered out on extensions of the boiler frame. Now the men from Flemington Street, Glasgow, could not allow their brain-child to receive a name connected with either Beyer Peacock, or Kitson, so they chose a good Scottish name and dubbed their invention a 'Modified Fairlie', although the only thing it had in common with the original Fairlie type was in being a double bogie steam locomotive. NBL's sales department thought up some rather dubious reasons as to why a 'Modified Fairlie' was the best type of articulated yet evolved, and Col Collins was persuaded to try the things out, doubtless with plenty of reminders about good relationships enjoyed in the past, and dire warnings about putting all the eggs in that Sassenach firm's Garratt basket.

Collins was suitably impressed with these arguments, and as a result schemes (a) and (b) above were ordered both as Garratts and as 'Modified Fairlies', although the Garratt, being the established type, was given the larger quantities. As the third and fourth articulated classes, the Garratts were GC and GD while the others were allocated F for Fairlie and classed FC and FD, the second letters thus corresponding.

115

Meanwhile, while the SAR were trying out their GA and GB Garratts, the New Cape Central Railway, which ran from Worcester to Mosselbaai, purchased two Garratts, these being essentially an enlargement of the GB class, having the same wheel arrangement and possessing the same technical features. In service, each replaced two of the old 7th class 4—8—0s, the 95 ton Garratt doing the work of 166 tons of tender engines and at the same time saving 5 tons of coal and one engine crew's wages. In 1925, when the NCCR was absorbed by the SAR, these two engines became Class GK and were finally scrapped in 1957, their final years being spent on the Donnybrook to Underberg branch.

These NCCR Garratts formed the basis for the GC class, and apart from the cylinders, which were smaller on the SAR version, the designs were almost identical. Additionally, North British, in their 'Modified Fairlie', were required to maintain the maximum amount of standardisation with the competing Garratt, and all major dimensions tallied, that is cylinder and wheel sizes, wheel spacing, boiler dimensions, etc, and it would appear that most of the motion details were also interchangeable. Thus, Collins was strictly trying like for like, the only differences between the GC and FC being those essentially due to the different systems of articulation. Six GC were supplied, together with the solitary FC, the latter being scrapped in 1939 although the GCs lasted until 1964, working from Pietermaritzburg.

Similarly, of the larger size of locomotive, fourteen Garratts, Class GD, were built, together with four FD 'Modified Fairlies', and again the maximum degree of interchangeability was maintained between the two types, which were straightforward enlargements of the preceding classes. The FDs were scrapped during 1957—9, having spent their last days on the branch from Alicedale to historic Grahamstown, in the Cape. The GDs were used on a wide variety of services on the Cape branches, among which the most spectacular was the use of two GDs, double-heading over the Montagu pass from George to Oudtshorn, until replaced by larger Garratts. They were also used in Natal, from Durban and Pietermaritzburg, but the last few survivors, like their Fairlie equivalents, ended their days on the Grahamstown line where, in January 1968, only two or three remained in service. All are now withdrawn.

We now come to the larger designs outlined by Collins, both of which can be considered developments of the original GA, and which used an

(left) Storming up the Underberg branch in 1969, a pair of GCA Garratts head the mixed train from Donnybrook. A. E. Durrant

identical boiler design. In each case, inner carrying wheels were added to ease the passage through curves and in the case of the earlier design, the GE, more wheels of smaller diameter were provided, thus producing an engine with greater tractive effort on a lighter axle load. The resulting 2—8—2 + 2—8—2 was the second Garratt design with eight-coupled units, having been beaten by a short head by a solitary engine for Burma.

The second design, Class GG, was a straight development of the GA, but with larger driving wheels, for express working, plus of course the inner carrying wheels, making it a 2—6—2 + 2—6—2. The engine worked mail trains out of Cape Town, over the Hex River Pass, which has fifteen miles of 1 in 40, and in one test run the 9⅝ miles from Belleville Junction to Salt River were covered start to stop at an average speed of 46·3mph, the maximum speed being 57mph. To achieve this, the acceleration was quite phenomenal, but as Beyer Peacock did not boast about the load hauled on this occasion, it was presumably not particularly heavy.

In order to keep costs down, the cylinders were not enlarged to compensate for the increased wheel diameter, and as a result the engine was lacking in tractive effort, and was inferior to the '15CA' class of 4—8—2 which was introduced soon after on the same line. Thus, the GG was not repeated, and being non-standard, was scrapped in 1938, the boiler, like that of the GA, becoming a useful spare for the GE class. Both the GE and GG classes contained the same technical features as the GA, except where mentioned above.

So far, Garratt development on the SAR had proceeded in a reasonably ordered manner, but the years 1927—9 were typified by frenzied activity in the field of articulated locomotives, when things got rather out of hand, culminating in the resignation of Col Collins. It is difficult to know in which order to place the next seven new plus two sub types of articulated locomotives which appeared in that brief period, there being a number of inter-related factors.

It is probably best first to dispose of the GCA and GDA classes, both being direct descendants of the corresponding and earlier GC and GD designs. In both designs, German builders were favoured with the orders as by this time the original Garratt patents had expired, although Beyer Peacock generally kept ahead of competition by patenting their continuing developments in the form of pivots and steam-pipe joints. The GCA, GDA and the GF designs, all built in Germany, appear to have been produced without any co-operation from Beyer Peacock, as they were never referred to in that firm's catalogues, unlike those built in France, Belgium, Spain, etc, under licence and with full approval. Collins

117

*Hauling a load of sugar cane from Eshowe North,
GDA 2258 heads to Gingindlovu junction and the
mill at Amatikulu, in 1968.* A. E. Durrant

*A first series GE, with 'all-square' front tank, glints
in the evening sunshine at Gingindlovu, Natal, in
1968.* A. E. Durrant

*(left) In its last year of regular service, a GDA erupts
out of Alicedale with a mixed train for Grahamstown,
in 1967.* A. E. Durrant

GF 2427 heads the Saturday Donnybrook-Pietermaritzburg local passenger through Carthill, in 1968. A. E. Durrant

presumably sent complete sets of drawings out to international tender, which would hardly have pleased Beyer Peacock, and there may even have been some pressure from the Afrikaaner element in the SAR management, still sore from the Boer War, to order elsewhere than from Britain. Whatever the undercurrents were, some thirty-nine GCA Garratts were ordered from Krupp, and delivered in 1927 and 1928. These differed from the GC class in having round-topped instead of Belpaire fireboxes, while the front and rear water tanks had rounded corners at the sides, together with a large overall radius of the top sheet, compared with the all-square 'domestic cistern' tanks of the earlier Beyer Peacock Garratts. An additional two tons of coal were also carried, although the GC themselves later had their bunkers increased to conform.

The GCA have been popular little engines, capable of high speeds, despite their tiny wheels, and their longevity was probably assisted by the inclusion of bar frames instead of the GC's plate frames. For many years they worked the South Coast line from Durban, until realignment and bridge strengthening permitted their replacement by larger 4—6—2 and 4—8—2 unarticulated locomotives. A few were at Nelspruit, in the Eastern Transvaal, for the Sabie line, but in their later years the GCAs were based mainly at Pietermaritzburg for working the Mount Alida, Richmond, and Underberg branches. En route to

and from the sub-depots serving the branches, it was not uncommon to find the diminutive GCA double heading with a larger GF, or even a mighty GMA. Indeed, after main line services from Mason's Mill to Franklin had been dieselised, the last regular steam working, as far as Donnybrook, was the weekly local freight conveying a GCA from the Underberg line, and GF shunter from Donnybrook, to and from Mason's Mill for boiler washout. The last GCA worked until dieselisation spread to Underberg, starting in 1976. Latterly the GCAs assisted in their own destruction by hauling trains carrying the heavier rail needed to support even branch line diesels. A few GCAs were sold for industrial service, but none remain in use today.

The five GDA Garratts were built by Linke Hoffman in 1929, and like the GCAs were a direct development from their corresponding GD class, again having round-top fireboxes and rounded tanks, although the bunker capacity remained unaltered. The home of these engines has mainly been the Durban North Coast line based at Stanger and with a couple usually allocated to the Eshowe branch in Zululand. Right at the end, two were transferred to Port Elizabeth for the Grahamstown line; they were never popular and were soon relegated to work ballast trains, before withdrawal. Remarkably, two have been preserved, No 2257 outside Grahamstown station, and 2259 at De Aar; the latter is for sale.

Garratt and non-articulated combinations are generally uncommon, but this GF plus 19D pair were caught on the Barberton branch in 1969.
A. E. Durrant

What was for many years the most numerous Garratt class in the world was also produced in this period, the GF 4—6—2 + 2—6—4 which, with its adequate wheel diameter, plus outer four-wheeled bogies, made it a design more suited to higher speeds than the previous Garratts. The inner pony trucks, originally with inside bearings, now have outside frames and bearings.

All were built in Germany, by Hanomag, Maffei, and Henschel, in 1927—8, and were a distinct advance on previous SAR Garratts inasmuch as bar frames were used. Otherwise, the detailing was generally to the standards of the other German-built Garratts, the design being marred mainly by the use of old-type cylinders with Z ports and short-lap valves, which must have been specified by Collins, as standard German practice had long been straight ports and long lap. The GFs have, for forty years, been very useful engines on both main and branch lines, being a 'go-anywhere, do-anything' type of loco-motive, and were latterly to be seen on the two branches from Nelspruit, Durban North Coast, and on the secondary routes and branches radiating north and south of Pietermaritzburg. From Franklin to Kokstad they worked the daily passenger train, but elsewhere they were on freight and mixed trains, and seen in pairs double-headed, or assisting a GMA, on both the Franklin and Greytown routes. Two were scrapped prematurely, due to accidents, and four

sold to Mozambique, but the remainder lasted well into the 1970s on SAR, while several have been sold for industrial work. The Enyati Railway in Natal has ten GFs for colliery use where they may be seen banked, double headed, or even, on rare occasions, triple headed! From 1979, they have been fitted with extraordinary diesel-driven air compressors, mounted behind the bunkers, for actuating the air brakes on SAR's coal export block trains, some of which originate on the Enyati line. For details see the end of this chapter. Other SAR trains are normally vacuum braked.

We now come to a point where Col Collins seems to have shown remarkable indecision and lack of direction. Having tried out the 'Modified Fairlie' against the Garratt and, quite rightly, favoured and re-ordered the latter in both the modified types and the new GF class, he split an order for twenty eight-coupled articulateds delivered in 1927. Ten of these were further GE Garratts, built by Beyer Peacock and improved by having rounded topside corners to the front tanks, and a raised, inset bunker to give improved visibility. This was fine, the same boiler and motion were retained, and the policy of standardising Garratts continued.

Yet the other ten were ordered from Henschel and were again 'Modified Fairlies'! Furthermore, the same degree of disciplined standardisation was not adhered to as in the FC and FD classes

Climbing the Zululand escarpment, hauling empties for loading sugar cane, a second series GE, with round top front tank, passes a Zulu girl carrying her baggage in traditional manner! A. E. Durrant

and Henschel designed these 2—8—2 + 2—8—2 with a longer, thinner boiler, although the grate area was comparable. The engine units were nominally the same, having the same sized wheels and cylinders, and identical wheel spacing, the overall wheelbase differing by only 2in. One distinct improvement upon the GE was the use of bar frames, but of course these could have been incorporated easily on a Garratt. Even the classification system went awry, and the class was designated HF for 'Henschel Fairlie' instead of the FE which they should logically have received.

In 1928 Henschel produced a further HF, while in 1931 two more GE were built by Beyer Peacock, generally as the second series but with an increased cylinder diameter. The HF, which were used mainly on the Reef, were all withdrawn in 1950—1. The original batch of GEs were used on the difficult Johannesburg-Zeerust main line, but in latter years the class was concentrated on the North coast line from Durban, particularly at Stanger and Empangeni, where in addition to main line work they performed most of the work on the Eshowe and Nkwalini branches until replaced by more modern GEA and GO Garratts

in the 1970s. The first engine, No 2260, is preserved at Empangeni, although rather surprisingly, none were sold for colliery use, to which they would seem particularly suited. In latter years, the original six engines acquired a variety of bunker extensions, to an extent that possibly each was different.

Even now, the muddle is not all told, for the 'Union Garratt' comes upon the scene. In this, the front tank sits upon the leading engine unit, as on a normal Garratt, but the bunker and rear tank are cantilevered out on a boiler frame extension as on a 'Modified Fairlie'. Collins was persuaded to purchase a couple of classes, and typically of the muddled thinking prevailing one was classified 'U' for 'Union Garratt' while the other was GH!

J. A. Maffei were entrusted with the order for both types, each of which were for main-line use only, and had axle loads exceeding 18 tons, the first South African articulateds to come into this category. For some reason, the designs were not standardised to the extent which they might have been; for example, while both had the same grate area, the GH class had a typical short, fat

There is little coal left in the bunker as a GMAM nears the summit of Lootsberg pass with the Mossel Bay — Johannesburg passenger. In the 61 miles (98km) from Graaff Reinet, the Garratt has dragged its 13 coaches up 3,624ft (995m) in altitude, much of it at 1 in 40.   A. E. Durrant

Garratts and mountains were almost synonymous. A gleaming South African Railways class GMAM heads the Saturday afternoon passenger out of Ashton, with the Langeberg rising rampart-like on the horizon.   A. E. Durrant

A rare and unusual combination as GF Garratt and HF Modified Fairlie double-head a goods near Johannesburg in the 1930s. F. G. Garrison

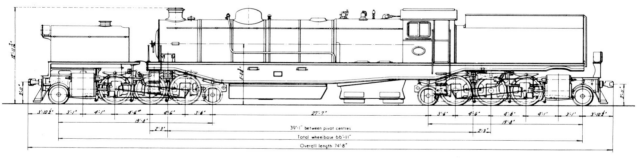

SAR Class U Union Garratt.

Garratt boiler, while the U boiler was longer and thinner. Both suffered from their proportions being basically unsuitable, the GF, which was a 4—6—2 + 2—6—4 with large wheels for express work, had the same defect as the GG, ie that with 50 per cent more adhesion weight than a conventional 4—8—2, the cylinders were too small to provide a commensurate tractive effort, so that the Garratt could not produce the increased low-speed performance and acceleration of which it was inherently capable.

The U class, a 2—6—2 + 2—6—2 freight engine, would again have been better as a 2—8—2 + 2—8—2, with the same boiler as the GH, and of course with larger cylinders. As it was, the U had no more tractive effort than the third series GE, but a much heavier restrictive axle load.

Both the U and the GH had bar-framed engine units, with Z-ported, short-lap cylinders. The boilers were of the round-top variety, and each had Duplex mechanical stokers, this feature of course being their *raison d'être*, although the stokers on the Us were later removed as unnecessary for the duties performed. The rear bunker carried coal only, and water was carried both in the normal front tank and in another slung underneath the boiler barrel. As with the 'Modified Fairlies', the cantilevered ends of the boiler frames caused heavy loads, both vertical and lateral, to be imposed upon the main pivots, leading to excessive wear. As a result, the two GH and ten U class engines were withdrawn from service long before their contemporary Garratts, the U class being used mainly on the reef and withdrawn 1952—7, while the GH ended up at Glencoe, in Natal, in 1957.

One of the most powerful steam locomotives in the Southern Hemisphere, an SAR class GL, ambles along from Glencoe to Vryheid before digging in its 89 000 lb tractive effort on the return load of coal.
A. E. Durrant

We now come to the final Garratt class produced under Col Collins, a class whose excellence compensates largely for some of the other machines which he caused to be perpetrated upon the SAR. Skipping Classes GI and GJ, which for some reason were never used, these GLs were at the time when they were built the largest locomotives in the whole of Africa, and the largest narrow-gauge locomotives in the world, a position which they maintained until 1955 when the EAR '59' class appeared. Even today they are by far the most powerful locomotives used on the SAR.

The GLs were built for the Natal main line which from Durban to Cato Ridge follows two routes, the original main line which has gradients of 1 in 30, and the re-located new main line which nevertheless has thirty-eight miles of almost continuous 1 in 66. The line had become a bottleneck.

In 1914, the same year, incidentally, that the first SAR Garratts were ordered, a decision had been made to electrify the Natal main line from Glencoe Junction through to Durban, where both the traffic and the gradients are the heaviest.

Both Garratts and electrification were delayed until after the war, and had the Garratts been available earlier, electrification would undoubtedly have been delayed for many years. However, in 1919, the Garratt was still a comparatively unknown quantity, while electrification was already established in a number of countries, and the 1914 decision was proceeded with. Construction work commenced in 1922, and in February 1925 partial electric haulage was instituted, from Estcourt to Ladysmith. This was soon extended, in both directions, until by June 1926 electric operation was in use from Glencoe to Pietermaritzburg. Three electric units per train were used on the heaviest freight trains, and with their load, two 14 class 4—8—2s were necessary to run each train between Pietermaritzburg and Durban. The GA Garratt was also in use by then, this being capable of taking the load hauled by two electrics. It became clear, that to avoid double-heading, a steam locomotive was required that would equal three electrics or two 14 class, such a proposal having been made as early as 1922.

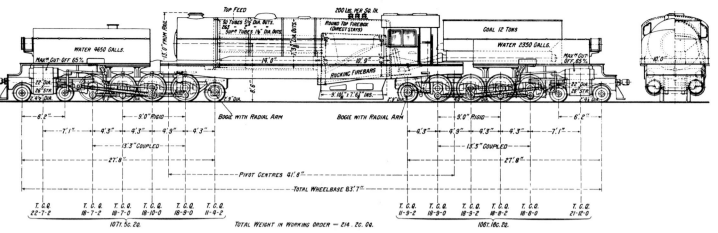

SAR Class GL Garratt.

Beyer Peacock were entrusted with the design of the GL class 4—8—2 + 2—8—4 to be built up to the maximum permissible total weight of 215 tons, with an axle load of 18½ tons. The GL was, of course, a stop-gap, the decision to electrify to the coast having already been taken, but the time factor would not allow the bottleneck to continue until this was implemented.

Some trepidation was naturally felt as to the possible success and stability of such a locomotive, whose outside boiler diameter was over twice the rail gauge and which would be, in one jump, 50 per cent larger and more powerful than the largest locomotives then operating, so caution was exercised and an initial order of only two locomotives placed.

The GLs were superbly designed. The engine units had bar frames with straight-ported cylinders, and long lap valves, included for the first time in South Africa. Despite the leading bogie, the drive was onto the third coupled axle of each unit, giving good long connecting rods, minimising their vertical forces at the crosshead. This feature, which helps to stabilise a large narrow-gauge engine, was introduced on the Benguela Railway Garratts, and later became a feature of Beyer Peacock Garratts. The immense boiler had a round-top firebox, containing thermic syphons and was, of course, mechanically stoked. Severe curvature had to be allowed for, the minimum radius being 275ft, while 300ft radius reverse curves with 4½in superelevation and no intermediate tangent provided even more severe conditions. Hence, the leading pivot was of the spherical type in place of the usual flat bearing, which of course was retained on the rear unit.

The first was placed in service in October 1929, by which time A. G. Watson was the CME, it being nominally of twice the power of a 14 class 4—8—2, having the same cylinder and wheel sizes. A slightly higher boiler pressure was used, to compensate for the maximum cut-off, which was limited to 65 per cent. On test, however, 1117 tons were hauled from Durban to Cato Ridge in 163 minutes, compared with 500 tons in 184 minutes which was the booked load for a 14 class.

This was well in excess of the 950 tons which three electrics were rated to haul onwards from Pietermaritzburg and this performance was achieved on half throttle and 45 per cent cut-off. The following day, a maximum load of 1205 tons was hauled over the same route, and subsequently, loads of 950 to 1000 tons were fixed, corresponding to the triple electric load, and worked at a higher speed. During these tests, the GLs were found to traverse the curves with exceptional smoothness and after thorough tests, lasting seven weeks, had been completed, an order for a further six engines was telegraphed for delivery in 1930, these having smoke deflecting cowls over the chimneys, for use in tunnels.

With these eight GLs in service, an adequate service was maintained until complete electric working to Durban was instituted in 1938, after which the GLs were transferred to Glencoe for working coal traffic thence from Vryheid, the smoke cowls then being removed. This section includes gradients of 1 in 50, up which 1200 ton trains are hauled, the work performed in the late 1960s being even harder than when they were first introduced, nearly forty years before! This line was converted to electric traction late in 1968, and the GLs were then transferred to Stanger for main line work to Empangeni. Traffic on this line had not then developed sufficiently to extend the GLs fully, and they were replaced by more modern, but less powerful GMA/Ms, although these had later to be double headed to cope with booming traffic. After being considered as hump shunting engines at Bloemfontein, the GLs were finally withdrawn in 1972, after over forty years of the heaviest work SAR had to offer. No 2350 was prematurely scrapped due to collision damage, but 2351 has been preserved at De Aar. 2352 was also earmarked for preservation, and in magnificent condition, ran up to Germiston under her own steam in 1972; after eight years of neglect she is now up for sale.

127

Garratts and mountains go together. The Hottentots-Hollands range forms an impressive backdrop for this GEA heading towards Cape Town with a trainload of Elgin apples for export.   A. E. Durrant

The new CME, A. G. Watson, was, unlike his predecessor, not an advocate of articulated power, and apart from the second GL batch, not a single 3ft 6in-gauge Garratt or any other type of articulated locomotive was ordered during his term of office.

There was thus a gap until 1938, when a further CME, W. A. J. Day, was faced with the problem of handling traffic between Johannesburg and Zeerust, on the main line to Mafeking and Rhodesia, where 60lb track was laid and 1 in 40 gradients abounded, some of them almost continuous for seventeen miles. The engines used on the section included 19D 4—8—2s, GE and GF Garratts, plus Watson's solitary 21 class 2—10—4, none of which was adequate, the best combination of power and speed being double-headed 19Ds.

(left) A far cry from the small tank engine often associated with the term 'industrial locomotive'; Douglas Colliery used a ex-SAR class GM to heave 40 bogie trucks out of SAR's yard at Vandyksdrift. On the return trip with 40 'loads', a 4—8—2 tender engine will provide assistance.   A. E. Durrant

It was thus decided to introduce a Garratt equal to two 19Ds and a design was worked out, using a shortened GL boiler. This proved to be too heavy for the civil engineer's peace of mind, and an unprecedented step was taken, that of reducing the water capacity to a minimum, and carrying the main supply in an auxiliary water tank. The civil engineer, presented with this, agreed to the axle load on the coupled wheels being substantially higher than otherwise allowed on this track. The front tank held only sufficient water for shunting purposes, and the rear unit held coal only. In all other technical respects, the design followed that of the GL class.

Sixteen locomotives were built by Beyer Peacock in 1938 classified as GM, and they revolutionised working on the Zeerust line, on which they spent most of their working lives. After electrification of the West Rand lines, they were stationed at Krugersdorp, working to Mafeking, mainly on freight, in later years, after the introduction of the GMA/M class. When the Mafeking line was dieselised in 1972, the GMs

GEA 4009, known as Renoster (Rhinoceros), *with experimental spark arresting apparatus, blows down before hauling the morning goods out of Caledon, December 1969.* A. E. Durrant

were transferred to Pretoria and Pietersburg to work the northern Transvaal main line, where they were not popular, and were used only when necessary. In mid 1973 they were withdrawn from service, but soon afterwards an acute power shortage at Breyten developed, and three GMs were hastily overhauled at Capital Park and despatched to Breyten, from whence they worked to Piet Retief. After about a year, they became somewhat run down, and were mainly to be found on the Spitzkop colliery shunt. During this period while they ran from Breyten, about two years, they never appeared on SAR's official 'motive power position' returns, being officially non-existent! All three resuscitated locomotives were sold to collieries and although no longer at work, could at any time be overhauled and reused. As forerunners of SAR's most numerous and successful classes, the GMA/M, it is a pity that no GM was kept for preservation.

No further Garratts were supplied to South Africa during the war, although Beyer Peacock produced them for other countries in Africa, but immediately after cessation of hostilities SAR ordered no less than fifty new Garratts, the largest single Garratt order ever placed. These 4—8—2 + 2—8—4s were designed also for 60lb track, but in order to eliminate the auxiliary water tank, were much smaller engines. As the same overall boiler dimensions as for the GE class were used, they were, rather quixotically, considered as a development of that class, and

designated GEA. The boiler, however, was not the same, having a round-top firebox while elsewhere the design was entirely changed. The wheel arrangement was of course different, the frames of bar type, and the driving wheels larger.

Despite these generally enhanced dimensions, the GEAs were hand fired, and on some of the arduous duties to which they were entrusted they represent the limit of a fireman's endurance. These were the first Garratts on the SAR to have the 'streamlined' tanks which Beyer Peacock introduced after the war, while the bunkers exhibit variations. No 4009 underwent an extra-ordinary transformation late in 1967, having a new spark arresting chimney fitted experimentally. This consisted of a horizontal extension stretching right over the front tank, with a turned up end, the whole ensemble resembling very closely those monstrosities designed by M. Petiet of the French C.F. du Nord in the 1860s.

The GEAs were at first used on various lines throughout South Africa, including that to Mafeking, and from Pietermaritzburg, but for most of their lives they have been associated with three areas. In Natal, they worked freight traffic on the South coast line, but were more commonly found on the North coast on the main line to Empangeni, later migrating to the Eshowe and Nkwalini branches when displaced by GMAMs. One of their final duties was to shunt the sugar mill at Felixton, and this produced one of Natal's more remarkable sights, not as far as is known,

*The first GMA/M, No 4051, approaches Rooihoogte
with a freight from Graaf Reinet, over the Lootsberg
pass, at the end of steam operation on this line.*
A. E. Durrant

captured on film. At the end of each shift, the
engine returned to shed at Empangeni, and with
line capacity at a premium, instead of running
light, it was usually coupled on ahead of the next
train, which in those days, was probably double
headed by Garratts, making a triple header!

The GEAs were best known for the fifteen
engines which worked the lines from Mossel Bay
to Riversdale, and to Oudtshoorn via the
Montagu Pass, including the passenger trains,
run in daylight and easily photographed. A
solid quarter century of hard work was put in,
hauling heavy loads over gradients as steep as 1
in 36, until replaced by GMAMs in 1974. The last
GEAs were also in Cape Province, which
eventually had twenty-four, nearly half of the
class, stationed at Cape Town to work the
Caledon line over the steep Sir Lowry's and Houw
Hoek mountain passes. The highlight was the
annual apple season, when frequent specials were
operated from Elgin to the cooling plant in Cape

Town docks, before the apples were exported. The
specials were always assisted over Sir Lowry's
pass, usually by 4—8—2s, at first as bankers, and
later double headed with Garratts; 1975 was the
last apple season entirely steam powered, but a
few GEAs were steamed up in 1976, the last in
regular SAR use.

After some time in store, most GEAs have
been scrapped, but some are being offered for
sale. So far five are in colliery use, including two
magnificent blue examples at Vryheid Coronation
Colliery.

Following the GEAs, the SAR returned to the
GM concept of large boiler, mechanical stoker,
and auxiliary water tanks, in three classes built in

*(overleaf) Garratts of two gauges. On 29 November
1980, to celebrate the centenary of South Africa's
Durban-Pietermaritzburg line, SAR ran a
commemorative special hauled by two GMAM
Garratts. Here they are seen passing Umlaas Road
station, with a class NGG13 2ft gauge Garratt in
attendance. A. A. Jorgensen*

131

the 1950s which turned out to be SAR's final 3ft 6in-gauge Garratts. All three classes had Commonwealth cast-steel bed frames manufactured in the USA, with Franklin spring-loaded wedge horns. Roller bearings were used throughout, cannon boxes on all axles except for the inner radial trucks, which had outside bearings. In order not to overstress the rails, the balancing was arranged to give a maximum hammerblow of 1 ton per wheel at 45mph.

The boiler unit frame is of welded I section, and has mounted upon it the HT mechanical stoker. The firebox itself is all-welded, and uses a U shape foundation ring as introduced by Bulleid on his Pacifics for the Southern Railway. Thermic syphons, as fitted to the earlier GM class, were suppressed, although certain drivers prefer the syphon-equipped GMs as being better steamers.

Two of the new classes were of the same nominal dimensions as the pre-war GMs, and the lighter of these, which had slightly increased coal and water capacities, were designated GMA. For main-line work, where more coal and water is required, and axle load restrictions are less severe, the GMAM class was introduced. However, to suit the various lines on which they are used, some GMAM have been converted to GMA, while a few GMA have reverted to GMAM, the modifications required being simple. Those GMAMs built for use on the East London main line had steam-operated smoke deflecting cowls over the chimneys for use in tunnels but, since the dieselisation of this line, the cowls have been removed, leaving the rather truncated chimney visible. No less than 120 GMA and GMAMs were built from 1953 to 1958, making them by far the most numerous class of Garratt in the world.

It seems the fate of the GMA/M class to be steam's last stand on many lines about to be dieselised or electrified. With so numerous a class, the list of lines worked is numerous; apart from the East London line, they worked the Witbank-Germiston coal traffic, and the main Eastern Transvaal line through Waterval Boven until electrified. Some assisted the GLs on the Glencoe-Vryheid line, where they were regularly double headed. Also in Natal, there was the biggest concentration of Garratt power in South Africa, where, just before dieselisation, Mason's Mill shed at Pietermaritzburg had an allocation of 101 Garratts, of which 74 were GMA/Ms! The incredible thing about this operation was that such a concentration of massive motive power was for use on two branch lines — south to Franklin and north to Greytown. Both lines ran parallel to the coast, crossing numerous river valleys, and were generally climbing or descending on 1 in 30 grades. Two GMA/Ms were needed per 900 ton train, and on the Greytown

line, a train in one direction would encounter an opposing train at most passing loops — usually also hauled by double Garratts! GCA, GF, and GMA/M were double headed in various combinations, the staccato beat of the GMA/Ms invariably completely drowning the softer waffle of the older Garratts. The sight and sound of two GMA/Ms battling up the 1 in 30 to Claridge summit, with full load, perhaps slipping in the frost of a winter dawn, will never be forgotten by those who have experienced it. No tame preservation railway, however polished their locomotives, can ever provide such an orgasmic thrill to the beholder!

South of Maritzburg, trains were less frequent, but included passenger workings and generally more photogenic scenery, into wilder and less accessible locations dotted with circular Zulu huts, so that the attractions were about equal. Just south of Donnybrook the narrow gauge line from Umzinto shares a section of three-rail mixed-gauge track, where it was possible to see Garratts of two gauges on the same line. Upon dieselisation of these lines, most of the GMA/Ms moved to the North coast line, where again they often double headed with each other, or with the smaller GO class. Some went south to Mossel Bay in 1974, replacing GEAs, and by mid 1978 the Cape Midland division had 59 GMAMs, plus 19 in the Cape Western at Worcester, which between them hauled most of the traffic over 930km of secondary main line, including the Montagu and Lootsberg mountain passes, plus many other exceptionally severe gradients. These lines, too, succumbed to dieselisation, mainly in 1979, although two diesels are invariably needed to equal the performance of one GMAM. The other main area of GMA/M operation was the Krugersdorp-Mafeking main line, which they shared with their GM predecessors, until also dieselised.

As useful and powerful units of motive power, the GMA/Ms are constantly being found new spheres of operation. When the rural branch from Derwent to Stoffberg was extended to the ore workings at Roossenekal, the light 4—8—2s were at first double headed to work heavier traffic. The line was then realigned and relayed with heavier track, and heavy 4—8—2s of classes 15CB, 15CA, and then 15F introduced. Finally, just before electrification, GMA/Ms were drafted in, at first double headed with 4—8—2s, then eventually run as double Garratts. Another line which has seen much GMA/M activity is the cross country line from Waterval Boven south through Breyten to Vryheid in Natal. By the mid 1960s, GMA/Ms were used throughout this route, but by 1977, the conversion of the Ermelo-Vryheid section to form part of the heavy rail, electrified, Richard's Bay coal export line, had displaced most of the steam, except for the small pocket north of Ermelo. Even here, traffic had declined because of the opening of an alternative electrified route, yet in 1980, another double Garratt working started! The new colliery at Witrand just south of Carolina, rails its coal north, and what had been the Carolina local goods, lightly loaded behind a single GMA/M, suddenly became a heavy freight including coal traffic, and hauled by a pair of Garratts — a *new* double Garratt working in the 1980s!

Late in 1979, a locomotive shortage in Zimbabwe-Rhodesia, coupled with the need to reduce diesel working to conserve oil, brought more GMA/Ms back into service, when 21 were hired to the National Railways of Zimbabwe (NRZ) working from Bulawayo to Wankie and Gwelo. As of November 1980, eight GMA/M have been hired to work the Beira line in Mozambique, while some are scheduled to take over from 19D 4—8—2s on the Mafeking-Vryburg line on SAR, so that this modern class, constantly being displaced in its prime of life, is still being found useful work. Two have been sold for industrial work, and seven scrapped due to collisions, which seem to occur rather frequently on SAR's busy, single track, routes. Undoubtedly, the money spent buying diesels, in a country with plenty of coal but no oil, would have been far better spent doubling the track, and getting better utilisation out of existing steam power and rolling stock.

The GO class are in all technical points the same as the GMA and GMAM classes, but in order to reduce the weight, smaller boilers are provided, and smaller cylinders are also therefore used. Nevertheless, it is interesting to note that the all-up weight of a GO is about the same as the pre-war GM, despite the latter being a larger loco-motive. This is the price paid for such structural and operational improvements as cast-steel beds and roller bearings. The GOs, like their heavy GMA/M equivalents, have tanks and bunkers of a rather bulbous 'streamlined' design. Originally used on various sections of SAR, the GOs spent most of their working life concentrated on the Belfast-Steelport branch in the Eastern Transvaal, being stationed at Lydenburg. One of the hardest lines on SAR, from a nadir of 2427ft (740m), the line climbs in 95 miles (152km), to the summit at Nederhorst which, at 6875ft (2096m), is the highest point on SAR. The ruling gradient is 1 in 33, up which the fierce crackle of a GO's staccato exhaust, syncopating in and out of syn-chronisation, had no equal. When the line was dieselised in 1972 (invariably using two or three diesels per train), the GOs were sent to the

(right) Sugar cane from Eshowe rolls down the 1 in 30 grades on Zululand's most scenic branch line, with a class GO at the head end.   A. E. Durrant

135

Transkei, where they were not liked, being too small to replace two 14CRB 4—8—2s, and longer in the coupled wheelbase, taking less kindly to the sharp curves in the Kei River crossing. Accordingly, they were drafted almost immediately to Natal, sometimes being 'borrowed' by Mason's Mill on the way down, and put to work on the North coast. From Empangeni and Stanger, they worked the main line, the Eshowe and Nkwalini branches, replacing GEs, and the line north to the Swaziland frontier at Gollel, where they replaced various 19th class 4—8—2s. South of Empangeni, they often double headed either with a GMA/M or another GO, to produce the most ear shattering sound SAR has heard. From 1975 they were replaced by diesels, since when the whole class has been rotting away at De Aar, modern and effective motive power prematurely withdrawn in order to further the insane policy of *increasing* the country's dependence on imported fuel!

SAR Narrow Gauge

The narrow gauge, of 2ft 0in, owned by the SAR, is naturally of less importance than the 3ft 6in gauge system, but it might have had priority in this chapter, Garratts having been supplied earlier than for the main line, to wit in 1919.

The first 2ft 0in-gauge Garratts, Class NGG11 were, like the GA class, of the 2—6—0 + 0—6—2 type, but in keeping with what was thought good enough for the narrow gauge, they were not superheated, and had ordinary flat slide valves.

Three of these little Belpaire-boilered engines were built, and their performance was considered extraordinarily satisfactory, and to a large extent they influenced the further trials of Garratts on the 3ft 6in gauge. Numbered NG51—53, two were scrapped in the 1960s after over forty years of service, but No NG52 was sold to the Rustenberg Platinum mines where, as No 7, resplendent in blue livery, it was still occasionally steamed up until 1970.

Following the success of Nos NG51—3, a further two were built in 1925, but in this case they were superheated and fitted with piston-valve cylinders. Like the earlier engines, they were first used on the Umzinto to Donnybrook line, which abounds in curves down to 150ft radius, and gradients of 1 in 33, a heavy traffic of timber and sugar cane being carried. When replaced by larger Garratts they were transferred to the Estcourt-Weenen branch, and by 1967 had been relegated to shunting at Port Elizabeth. Both are now withdrawn.

The next class, NGG12, built by Franco-Belge under licence, was intended for the Upington-Kakamas branch, off the main line to South West Africa, which was laid with track as light as 20lb

per yard, and also the Fort Beaufort to Seymour branch, laid with similar light track, one Garratt being allocated to each branch.

These miniscule 2—6—2 + 2—6—2 Garratts successfully handled far greater loads than their 4—4—0 predecessors and as a result the branches prospered.

Accordingly, two years later, Hanomag supplied a third Garratt, Class NGG14, which was very slightly larger. Despite their small size all these little locomotives were superheated, piston-valve jobs, and had round-top boilers and plate frames. The NGG14 was originally sent to the Seymour line, but when, in 1940, this was converted to 3ft 6in gauge both the Garratts used thereon were sent to the Kakamas branch, where they lasted until that too was widened in 1949. Upon this, the two NGG12 were sold to the Rustenburg Platinum Mines, who numbered them 5 and 6, scrapping them in 1959. The NGG14 was sent to the Estcourt-Weenen section upon which it ran for a while until replaced by the older but more powerful superheated NGG11, when the small engine was scrapped.

We now come to the main 2ft 0in-gauge Garratts, Classes NGG13 and NGG16, the two classes being so similar that there seems no point in classifying them separately. In fact, there are greater variations between the earlier and later versions of the NGG16 than there are between the NGG13 and subsequent NGG16.

These engines were designed for the principal narrow-gauge branches, which have 35lb rail, this being little lighter than the 40lb track used on certain 3ft 6in-gauge lines, and in fact these 2ft gauge engines are little smaller than the GB class.

First built by Hanomag in 1927, these engines have, like all the 2ft 0in-gauge Garratts, outside frames, although for the first time they were of the bar type. Superheaters were of course provided, and piston-valve cylinders, while the boiler was of the round-top type. The NGG13 class have plain bearings throughout, while the NGG16 have roller bearings on the carrying axles, this being the only significant difference between the two classes.

The twelve NGG13s were followed by eleven NGG16s before the war. Then, in 1951, a fourth batch of seven was supplied. In 1959, seven more were built for the Tsumeb Corporation in South West Africa, but because the gauge was being changed to 3ft 6in, these engines were diverted new to the SAR. The Tsumeb batch differed in having increased coal and reduced water supplies, an auxiliary water tank being used, as on the main-line GM series. Finally, in 1965, a further eight of this type were ordered, and as Beyer Peacock were on the verge of closing down and unable to fulfil the contract, it was awarded to the

(above) SAR's second batch of NGG11s were superheated, and externally distinguishable by piston valves and improved cabs. They survived at Port Elizabeth until about 1970, and NG 54 is shown at Humewood Road shed.   A. E. Durrant

(below) SAR's very first Garratts were the initial, slide valve, batch of class NGG11. One of these survives, having been sold to Rustenberg Platinum Mines, where it is seen in steam in 1967. At the moment it is 'preserved' in doubtful fashion, but it is important that this engine, as a forerunner of the World's largest Garratt fleet, should be suitably renovated and protected for posterity.
A. E. Durrant

(above) The earlier NGG16s were distinguished by round top front tanks of rivetted construction, as on the NGG13 class. NG 109 rolls along with an apple train, in 1968.   A. E. Durrant

(below) Brand new in 1968! A Hunslet Taylor NGG16 winds along the Umzinto-Donnybrook line soon after being placed in service.   A. E. Durrant

Hunslet Engine Co, who assembled them at their South African associates, Messrs Hunslet Taylor & Co (Pty) Ltd. Two were delivered late in 1967, and the remaining six were put into service during 1968. The basic class has thus been in production on and off for forty years, a great tribute to the original design. This final batch up to now have been the last Garratts built anywhere in the world and it is a strange coincidence that the last, like the first, are for the 2ft 0in-gauge.

The NGG13 and 16 classes worked both the Port Elizabeth to Avontuur section, 177 miles (283km) long, which carries heavy seasonal fruit traffic, plus an equally heavy all-year limestone traffic to the Eastern Province Cement Works. From 1975, a class of narrow gauge diesels replaced the Garratts on the inner workings, leaving the steam workings to the NG15 class 2—8—2s. The remaining forty narrow gauge Garratts are now concentrated in Natal, where the four 2ft gauge branches (Estcourt-Weenen, Mid Illovo, Umzinto-Donnybrook, and Port Shepstone-Harding) are entirely Garratt worked. These narrow gauge Garratts bid fair to be the last in operation on SAR, especially since the oil crisis has caused some traffic to revert from road to rail, although SAR myopia could well negate this, one way or another. These little engines will haul 183 short tons up a 1 in 33 gradient, and on the easier sections, loads of up to 425 tons are handled. Furthermore, they are by no means slow, and can bowl happily along at about 40mph. Their introduction has saved the expense of converting these narrow-gauge lines to 3ft 6in, and as the traffic carried is largely export, in the case of the Avontuur line, or internal, the bogey of transhipment is almost absent and these lines, with their newly-built Garratts, are likely to stay narrow for a long time.

Industrial Garratts

The 1977 oil crisis, plus its subsequent escalations, alerted South African industry to the high cost and possible unavailability of diesel fuel, and indeed, the South African government exhorted industry to save oil wherever possible. One way to do this was to reduce dependence on diesel locomotives, and over the last few years, about ten or a dozen mines, formerly either dieselised or committed to dieselise, have reversed policy to retain, or even re-introduce steam traction. Clearly, this is in the shareholder's, as well as the country's interest, and has resulted in a large number of additional Garratts finding themselves in industrial service. Conversely, South African Railways, although a government enterprise, completely opposes national policy, and upon the deposition of the Shah of Iran (SA's major oil supplier at the time), immediately placed further large orders for diesel locomotives!

Only three Garratts were built for industrial use in South Africa, but many more were sold by SAR, and also by Rhodesia Railways, for use by South African industry, particularly for colliery work where heavy trains require haulage over steep gradients, over distances ranging from a kilometre or two to about 15km. The steady electrification and dieselisation by SAR, over the last decade, have released large numbers of Garratts which are sold by tender to further users. Among these are Dunn's Locomotive and Boiler Works, at Witbank, centre for the Transvaal coalfield, an organisation which buys, sells, hires, and overhauls locomotives for industrial use. Apart from Garratts sold directly to industry, others are thus owned by Dunn's and hired out to various sites. Thus the following account of industrial Garratts in South Africa is subject to considerable change as time goes on. In particular, with many South African mines halting and even reversing previous dieselisation policies due to the oil crisis, further Garratts may yet appear in industrial service, and further sites appear on the list of users.

Of the three Garratts built for industrial use, the first, BP 6206/25, was to the same general design as supplied to the New Cape Central Railway, SAR class GK 2—6—2 + 2—6—2, and this led to the industrial Garratts being referred to erroneously as GKs. The two later examples, BP 6353/27 and 6780/35 were in fact much larger than the GK class, the earlier engine for the Dundee Coal Co being the prototype of a class eventually supplied also to two railways in Spain, suitably altered to metre gauge, as well as a further example in South Africa. All other industrial Garratts were from main line sources, and it is convenient to list these geographically. Some of the operation, particularly on colliery railways, is quite spectacular, with assorted combinations of Garratt and 'straight' engines heaving coal out from low lying mine workings.

TRANSVAAL

Blesbok Colliery, Broodsnyersplaas

No 3. Ex SAR GCA 2624, purchased 1966. Currently derelict.

New Clydesdale Colliery, Bezuidenhoutsrust

No 2, industrial Garratt BP 6780/35, ex New Raleigh Colliery. Colliery worked by Transvaal Navigation Co from mid 1970s, and locomotive scrapped about 1978. Various other TNC Garratts have, and do, work into New Clydesdale.

Although Garratts are extensively used in mine service, only three were actually built for industrial use. Transvaal Navigation Colliery No 2 rolls coal from the mine to SAR's interchange siding at Bezuidenhoutsrust, about 1975.   A. E. Durrant

Transvaal Navigation Collieries, Bezuidenhoutsrust

This mine took over New Clydesdale from the mid 1970s, this being a convenient arrangement as they shared a 'main line' from a junction and yard near the mines, to the SAR exchange sidings. Locomotives were then pooled, and used indiscriminately on either mine, but both locomotive sheds were used for a while, the Clydesdale shed closing about 1977–78. By coincidence, both the large industrial Garratts were then under the same ownership, while further ex main line Garratts were acquired until at the peak of steam operations there were five Garratts of four different types. Details are:

TNC No 2, industrial Garratt BP 6353/27, ex Dundee Coal Co. Scrapped about 1978.

Industrial Garratt BP 6780/35, absorbed from New Clydesdale. Scrapped about 1978.

609, ex RR 16th class 609, on hire from Dunn's during the mid 1970s, returned to Dunn's.

Ex-SAR GM 2304 hired from Dunn's 1977, returned to Dunn's about 1978.

Ex-SAR GF 2433 purchased 1975, still in use.

The mine ordered two diesels just before the first oil crisis, but the soaring price of oil has made further diesel purchases an illogical absurdity, and currently there are two diesels, one 4–8–2, and the remaining GF Garratt, with any two locomotives in use daily.

Tweefontein United Collieries, Minnaar

This mine has never actually owned a Garratt, but two have been hired from Dunn's at different dates. Due to the heavy work involved in bringing coal out of the valley, double heading was common, and the smaller GF Garratt was often paired with assorted other power. The large GM Garratt, being mechanically stoked, was used only briefly, and indeed such an engine is probably unsuitable for mine work unless used in the long term, with suitable training for the firemen.

Ex SAR class GM, 2304. Used briefly during 1977.

Ex SAR class GF, identity not positively established, used from 1977 to 1979.

With the rolling Zululand hills faint in hazy background, 2ft gauge NGG13 Garratt heads a train on the branch from Ixopo to Madonela, on the Transkei border. The track on this narrow gauge branch is better than main lines in many parts of the world.
A. E. Durrant

Returning to 'Maritzburg from the Greytown line, a GF and GMAM combination battle with the vicious S-bend, set on a 1 in 30 gradient, leading to the final summit at Claridge. A. E. Durrant

Consolidated Main Reef Mines and Estates Ltd, Langlaagte

A large gold mining operation in the West Rand, near Johannesburg, which acquired industrial Garratt BP 6780/35 new from Beyer Peacock. This may have been too powerful, for it was sold fairly soon to New Raleigh Colliery. Mine running number 1, later No 5.

New Douglas Colliery, Vandyksdrift

No 3, ex RR 16th class 603, worked from 1964 to 1975, when it was sold to Dunn's in part exchange for a GM.
No 604, ex RR 16th class, on hire from Dunn's 1973—74.
No 2301, ex SAR GM class, worked from 1975 to 1977, using a tender ex-Mallet MC1 1643 instead of the standard auxiliary water tank. Very heavy work on this colliery, with regular banking or double heading of loads from the mine. Two diesels were purchased in 1977, but the GM remains on the premises, although requiring heavy overhaul.

New Raleigh Colliery

Industrial Garratt BP 6780/35, sold to New Clydesdale. Mine closed.

Rustenburg Platinum Mines Ltd, Rustenburg

An extensive and expanding operation in the Northwest Transvaal, originally served by a 2ft gauge system, which at one time used three ex-SAR Garratts. These were replaced by diesels, but the narrow gauge set-up seems likely to be replaced in turn by the expanding 3ft 6in-gauge network, where steam is replacing diesel!
No 5, ex SAR NGG 12 No 56, bought about 1955, scrapped 1959.
No 6, ex SAR NGG 12 No 57, bought about 1955, scrapped 1959.
No 7, ex SAR NGG 11 No 52, bought 1958, still in reserve 1967, and now 'preserved' after a fashion near Johannesburg. This is a very important locomotive, being the only survivor of SAR's first batch of Garratts; hopefully this may be recognised and a better form of preservation instituted.

South African Coal Estates, Landau Colliery, Blackhill

No 1, Ex RR 16th class No 605, purchased 1964. A magnificent locomotive, normally immaculately maintained in maroon livery. From 1978/79 the mine's output has been by conveyor to the export coal loader, and this Garratt is up for sale as surplus to requirements.

South African Iron & Steel Corporation (ISCOR), Pretoria

No 20, ex SAR class U 1373, purchased about 1959 and subsequently scrapped.

NATAL

Dundee Coal and Coke Ltd, Wasbank

This mine was the purchaser of Beyer Peacock's first narrow gauge heavy industrial Garratt, No 6353/27. Burnside is close to Glencoe, but reached by a fairly lengthy branch from Wasbank. The mine was closed at an indeterminate date, and the Garratt sold to Transvaal Navigation Collieries. It was No 5 on the Dundee roster.

Durban Navigation Collieries (Durnacol), Dannhauser

As might be deduced from its title, DNC originally existed mainly for the supply of coal for bunkering ships at Durban. In the 1960s, as coal burning ships became fewer, the mine seemed to decline, but in the mid 1970s a new seam of metallurgical coal was discovered, the line extended to a new shaft, and the whole operation taken over by ISCOR. Increased traffic meant heavier motive power, and this included Garratts of various types, from time to time, thus:
618, ex RR 16th class 618, hired from Dunn's, dates unknown. Later to Enyati.
612, ex RR 16th class 612. Hired from Dunn's about 1973/4, and later fitted with Giesl ejector. The intention was to test against 618, but this was transferred to Enyati, and they never worked in competition. In 1977 the boiler unit of 612 was combined with the engine units off 608, overhauled at Dunn's, and the hybrid continued in use for a year or two until moved back to Dunn's.
Ex-SAR class GM 2303. Hired from Dunn's about 1976, and used for about two years, coupled to a tender from an old class 1 4—8—0, in lieu of an auxiliary water tank. Laid aside as heavy repairs became necessary, and replaced by 4168. Still on the premises.
4168, ex-SAR class GMAM 4168. Ex Dunn's early 1979, to replace 2303. The only GMAM in industrial use. Still at work, turn and turn about with two 15CB 4—8—2 tender engines.

The Enyati Railway

This is easily the most amazing colliery in Africa, possibly in the world, when it comes to railway operation. Enyati (also spelt Inyati, or Nyati) is the Zulu word for Buffalo, and probably indicates a prevalence for that beast before coal was worked in the area. The first mine was the Ammonium Colliery, opened in 1913 to exploit a type of coal particularly suited to the production of ammonia. This was served by a 2ft 0in-gauge railway from Boomlager station on the SAR. Soon after, coal was discovered at Inyati, and the Enyati Railway was built in 1918, the Ammonia railway being eventually replaced by a branch from 'The Nek', a junction and cramped marshalling yard below the peak of Pondwana. Today, Enyati is worked out, but coal is still loaded there by means of a cable railway from a mine across the valley at mount Ngwibi. A few years ago, there were hopper wagons in the dump lettered 'Buffalo', the English equivalent of Enyati, but how this fits into the history remains obscure!

Like most mining railways, operation commenced with tank engines, but due to the increase in traffic greater power was needed, at first realised by ten-coupled tank engines — Baldwin 2–10–2Ts. Ex-SAR tender engines were the next step, but by the 1970s Garratts started to become available, and at least fourteen Garratts of three classes have worked on the system in recent years. The uncertainty on quantities has been due to the hiring of engines from Dunn's, who operate many, perhaps most, of their locomotives incognito, with no clue as to origin.

Garratts started to appear on the premises about 1973/74, when GF 2371 arrived ex-SAR, and 16th class 618 ex RR. Both these were painted maroon at a time when the railway manager was Pat Lovell, an ex-Great Western fireman and RR driver who spoke Afrikaans to his drivers, Zulu to the natives, and English with a broad Bristol accent to your author! By 1978 there were six GFs (2371/77/86/87, 2404/08), and by the following year they had been joined by 2375/99, 2415/25, making a total of ten GFs. RR 618 was joined briefly by 606 ex Vryheid Coronation, and 1979 saw the acquisition of two GEA, 4020 and another believed to be 4050.

During 1979, SAR were starting to run their export coal traffic in block loads using air braked wagons, which meant locomotives being fitted with air brakes. As the traditional suppliers of air brake equipment were asking outrageously high prices for normal steam-operated pumps and accessories, Enyati started to fit their Garratts with equipment which on the surface seems quite ridiculous — diesel-driven air compressors on steam locomotives! On the GFs, this occupies the spare platform behind the bunker, but the GEAs and tender engines require a special compressor tender to accommodate this clumsy arrangement.

Operation on the Enyati can be quite spectacular, with multiple locomotives on one

train from time to time, according to loadings. Triple headed Garratts have been noted more than once, while normal operation sees loaded trains from the Nek hauled and banked by Garratts, sometimes using three locomotives. Furthermore, the railway runs through the most beautiful Zululand scenery, among rolling hills and valleys. For anyone looking for Garratt action in Africa today, Enyati must not be missed.

Hlobane Colliery

Originally the Vryheid Railway Coal and Iron Co, in later days this was known simply as Hlobane Colliery, serving the mine close to the station of that name. Up to about 1970 there was a fairly lengthy line serving the coking plants, but this is now closed. This was the first industrial line in South Africa to use a Garratt, buying a 2–6–2 + 2–6–2 to the New Cape Central (SAR GK) design new from Beyer Peacock, works No 6206/25. The heavy haulage was coal from the mine, which was set into a valley, up on to the plateau where a fairly level line ran to the coking plants. The GK was joined later by a heavy Baldwin 2–10–2T, and later again by an ex-SAR GCA Garratt which was rebuilt with 'streamlined' front and rear tanks to form what was nicknamed a 'GCB' class! The 'GCB' was ex-works about 1969, displacing the GK which was then scrapped. However, the ex-SAR Garratt lasted only a short time, and had disappeared by 1973. About 1976, before the first severe oil crisis, the mine bought a diesel for the remaining work, now confined to shunting trucks to and from the SAR sidings.

Vryheid Coronation Colliery

This is the third of the little group of Natal collieries, dealt with in alphabetical order, but coincidentally, also in geographical order, along the branch line from Vryheid to Hlobane, itself the name of a local mountain. Coronation Colliery mines on the slopes of Matshongololo and has its own main line, about 10km long, to the SAR at Hlobane station. After starting with the usual tank engines, output started to outstrip their capacity, and to date about five Garratts have been used. First was ex-RR 16th class No 606, soon followed by ex-SAR GCA 2193, both of which were very much in use during the late 1960s and early 1970s. Another, unidentified, GCA was also used during this period. In the mid-1970s, the railway then 'followed the fashion' and bought a Bo-Bo diesel-electric which then handled the main line traffic, using the RR 16th as standby power, and the tank engines to shunt the coke ovens. Came the 1977 oil crisis, and with diesel fuel getting prohibitively expensive, and

(above) *Vryheid Railway Coal & Iron Co No 2 was built to the drawings of the New Cape Central Railway Garratts (SAR class GK), themselves closely similar to SAR's GC class. In 1969, long after the GCs and GKs had been scrapped, the industrial version awaits its fate at Hlobane colliery, Natal.*
A. E. Durrant

(below) *A rare sight indeed is a train triple-headed by Garratts! Three GFs at Enyati, Natal, head empties to the mines from SAR's yard at Boomlager.*
A. E. Durrant

the diesel requiring very expensive spare parts, a GEA was bought from SAR. This was more or less run into the ground, and a second GEA was bought in 1980, as the first required heavy boiler repairs including retubing. It is understood that a third GEA is now being sought, possibly, and hopefully, to enable the mine to revert entirely to steam traction. The Vryheid Coronation loco-motive livery is an attractive blue, and apart from odd engines for royal specials, these are believed to have been the only Garratts to operate regularly in blue.

Industrial — other

As SAR, illogically, runs down its steam fleet, industrial users are quick to snap up bargains in motive power suitable for the use of South Africa's cheapest and most abundant source of energy. Hence, no matter now carefully this manuscript is updated by final press date, the chances are that yet further Garratts will be in use by the time the book appears on the shelves of booksellers. For those who are fascinated by Garratts, in this respect, the more out of date this volume is, the better!

LIST OF GARRATTS

SAR 3ft 6in GAUGE

Class	Locomotive Nos	Builder	Works Nos	Date
GA	1649, later 2140	BP	5941	1920
GB	1650, later 2166	BP	5942	1921
,,	2160-65	BP	6181-86	1924
GC	2180-85	BP	6187-92	1924
FC	2310, later 670	NBL	23140	1924
GCA	2190-2202	Krupp	970-82	1927
,,	2600-2625	,,	1043-68	1928
GD	2220-23	BP	6263-66	1925
,,	2228-34	,,	6281-87	1925
,,	2235-37	,,	6288-90	1926
FD	2320-3, later 671-4	NBL	23294-7	1926
GDA	2255-59	Linke H	3115-19	1929
GE	2260-65	BP	6193-98	1924-5
,,	2266-75	,,	6339-49	1926
,,	2276-77	,,	6716-17	1930
HF	1380-89	Henschel	20698-707	1927
,,	1390	,,	21052	1928
GEA	4001-50	BP	7168-7217	1945-7
GF	2370-2406	Hanomag	10512-48	1927-8
,,	2407-24	Henschel	21053-70	1928
,,	2425-34	Maffei	5748-57	1928
GG	2290	BP	6232	1925
GH	2320-21	Maffei	5687-88	1927
U	1370-79	,,	5673-82	1927
GK	(G1-G2 [NCCR]) (2340-41 [SAR])	BP	6135-36	1923
GL	2350-51	,,	6530-31	1929
,,	2352-57	,,	6639-44	1930
GM	2291-2306	,,	6883-98	1938
GMA/M	4051-75	Henschel	28680-704	1952
,,	4076-78	BP	7550-52	1956
,,	4079-83	,,	7677-81	1956
,,	4084-98	,,	7750-64	1956
,,	4099-4110	NBL	27691-702*	1956
,,	4111-20	,,	27769-78*	1958
,,	4121-30	BP	7836-45	1958
,,	4131-40	NBL	27783-92*	1958
,,	4141-70	Henschel	29600-29	1954
GO	2572-96	,,	28705-29	1954

*Beyer Peacock Nos 7765-76, 7826-35, and 7846-55 originally allocated before sub-contracting to NBL.

SAR NARROW GAUGE

Class	Locomotive Nos	Builder	Works Nos	Date
NGG11	NG51-53	BP	5975-77	1919
	NG54-55		6199-6200	1925
NGG12	NG56-57	Franco B.	2506-07*	1927
NGG13	NG49-50	Hanomag	10599, 10598	1928
"	NG58-69	"	10549-51	1927
"	NG77-83	"	10629-35	1928
NGG14	NG84	"	10747	1928
NGG16	NG85-88	Cockerill	3265-68	1937
"	NG109-116	BP	6919-26	1937
"	NG125-131	"	7426-32	1951
"	NG137-43(a)	"	7862-68	1958
"	NG149-56	Hunslet Taylor	3894-901	1967-8

*Beyer Peacock Nos 6365-66 allocated before sub-contracting.
(a) built as Tsumeb Corporation Nos TC6-TC12.

SOUTH AFRICA — 2ft 0in Gauge and Industrial

Class	Type	Cylinders Dia × Stroke (in)	Coupled Wheel Dia (ft in)	Boiler Press (psi)	Tractive Effort @75% (lb)	Grate Area (sq ft)	Max Boiler Dia (Ins) ft in	Heating Surface (sq ft) Fire-box	Tubes	Super-heater	Weights in Working Order (Tons) Max Axle	Ad-hesive	Total	Water Cpcty (Gal)	Fuel Cpcty (Tons/Gal)	Literature Reference
SAR 2ft 0in gauge																
NGG11	2-6-0 + 0-6-2	10½×16	2-6	180	15880	19·3	4-2	81·0	899	Nil	6·2	36·15	44·75	1350	2·5t	L25/20
NGG11	2-6-0 + 0-6-2	10½×16	2-6	180	15880	19·5	4-2	80·6	660·9	141·5	6·55	38·65	48·25	1350	2·5t	L139/25
NGG12	2-6-2 + 2-6-2	8½×16	2-6	180	10400	10·5	3-6⅜	45·0	378·5	97·5	3·75	22·5	36·0	1000	2t	
NGG13	2-6-2 + 2-6-2	12×16	2-9	180	18850	19·5	4-7¾	82·1	839·0	149·0	7·1	41·1	61·65	1825	4t	H3/36
NGG14	2-6-2 + 2-6-2	9×16	2-6	180	11664	10·5	3-6⅜	45·0	378·5	97·5	4·0	23·65	37·75	1000	2t	H5/36
NGG16	2-6-2 + 2-6-2	12×16	2-9	180	18850	19·2		75·0	845·0	147·0	6·9		60·55	1825	4t	L52/51
NGG16	2-6-2 + 2-6-2	12×16	2-9	180	18850	19·2		75·0	845·0	147·0	7·2		62·2	1825	4t	
Industrial 3ft 6in gauge																
—	2-6-2 + 2-6-2	17×22	3-6¾	180	40150	41·9		171·5	1835·5	448·0	14·0	81·7	114·75	3500	7t	L338/35

SOUTH AFRICAN RAILWAYS (3ft 6in Gauge)

Class	Type	Cylinders Dia × Stroke (in)	Coupled Wheel Dia (ft in)	Boiler Press (psi)	Tractive Effort @ 75% (lb)	Grate Area sq ft	Min Boiler Dia (Ins) ft in	Heating Surface (sq ft) Fire-box	Tubes	Super-heater	Weights in Working Order (Tons) Max Axle	Ad-hesive	Total	Water Cpcty (Gal)	Fuel Cpcty (Tons /Gal)	Literature Reference	Remarks
GA	2-6-0 + 0-6-2	18×26	4-0	180	47390	51·8	6-9	211·3	2343·2	526·5	17·75	104·7	133·85	4600	9t	L113/21	
GB	2-6-2 + 2-6-2	12×20	3-6¾	180	18190	23·3	4-5⅞	104·7	943·9	174·0	7·5 7·8	44·85 46·8	70·65 75·05	2000 2320	4t 4t	L32/25	1st Loco 2nd Order
GC	2-6-2 + 2-6-2	14×23	3-6¾	180	28470	34·0	5-2	156·8	1266·2	247·0	10·5	63·0	96·8	3000	5t	L33/25	
FC	2-6-2 + 2-6-2	14×23	3-6¾	180	28470	34·0	5-1¾	155·0	1232·0	280·0	10·5	62·9	99·7	3000	5t	L168/25	
GCA	2-6-2 + 2-6-2	14×23	3-6¾	180	28470	34·0	5-2	140·0	1226·0	226·0	10·8 11·7	65·25 66·85	102·65 105·8	3000	5t 7t		1st Order 2nd Order
GD	2-6-2 + 2-6-2	15×24	3-9½	180	32040	40·4	6-0	167·0	1510·0	360·0	12·75	75·35	114·05	3800	5t	L387/26	
FD	2-6-2 + 2-6-2	15×24	3-9½	180	32040	40·9	6-0	190·0	1555·0	362·0	12·35	72·85	114·1	3800	5t		
GDA	2-6-2 + 2-6-2	15×24	3-9½	180	32040	40·4	6-9	181·0	1560·0	360·0	13·7	79·55	119·85	3800	5t		
GE	2-8-2 + 2-8-2	19×24 18×24	3-9½	180	50850 46140	52·0	6-9	210·0	2360·0	390·0	13·45	103·5	148·4	4600	9t	L138/25 RE299/27	3rd Orders 1st & 2nd Orders
HF	2-8-2 + 2-8-2	18×24	3-9½	180	46140	53·0	5-11⅛	209·0	2079·0	577·0	13·1	102·8	150·05	4600	9t	L178/27	
GEA	4-8-2 + 2-8-4	18½×26	4-0	200	55620	51·3	6-9	212·0	2328·0	470·0	15·1	115·75	185·5	5600	10t	L56/46	
GF	4-6-2 + 2-6-4	16×26	4-6	185	34200	44·0	6-2	200·0	2045·0	465·0	14·2 14·0	84·0 82·5	145·55 143·25	4000	10t	RE327/28	2nd Order 1st Order
GG	2-6-2 + 2-6-2	18×26	4-9	180	39900	52·0	6-9	210·0	2366·0	390·0	16·2	94·5	147·75	4600	10t	L269/25	
GH	4-6-2 + 2-6-4	19½×26	5-0	180	44490	59·5	6-11	239·3	2403·4	641·0	18·1	107·5	184·75	6000	13·5t	L40/28	
U	2-6-2 + 2-6-2	18½×26	4-0	180	50050	59·5	6-1	198·0	2587·0	611·0	18·6	110·0	164·6	5280	14t	L208/27	
GK	2-6-2 + 2-6-2	15×22	3-6¾	180	31260	33·9	5-2	155·5	1530·5	300·0	10·5	63·0	94·9	3000	4t	L256/23	
GL	4-8-2 + 2-8-4	22×26	4-0	200	78650	74·5	7-0	340·0	3036·0	809·0	18·7	144·85	211·1	7000	12t	L340/32 L275/29	RE332/29
GM	4-8-2 + 2-8-4	20½×26	4-6	200	60700	63·5	7-0	281·0	2785·0	778·0	15·0	115·2	174·3	* 1600	10t	L32/39	*Plus 6750G Auxiliary Tank
GMA	4-8-2 + 2-8-4	20½×26	4-6	200	60700	63·5	7-0	241·0	2974·0	747·0	15·0	118·2	187·4	* 1650	11·6t	L77/55	*Plus 6810G Auxiliary Tank
GMAM	4-8-2 + 2-8-4	20½×26	4-6	200	60700	63·5	7-0	241·0	2974·0	747·0	15·35	120·8	191·75	* 2110	14t	L102/57	*Plus 6810G Auxiliary Tank
GO	4-8-2 + 2-8-4	18½×26	4-6	200	49200	56·6	6-2¾	231·0	2177·0	546·0	13·7	109·4	175·2	* 1650	11·2t		*Plus 6810G Auxiliary Tank

Chapter 9

Central Africa

This chapter covers the belt of countries stretching across Africa from Angola on the West to Mozambique on the East Coast, both being former Portuguese possessions. Between lie Zaïre (formerly Belgian Congo), Zambia (formerly Northern Rhodesia), Zimbabwe (formerly Southern Rhodesia and known simply as Rhodesia during its years of self declared independence in the 1960s and 70s), and the little State of Malawi (formerly Nyasaland). These countries share a gauge of 3ft 6in which, with the South African system, gives the whole of Southern Africa an integrated network of lines on that gauge, it being possible to travel from coast to coast by rail.

Zaïre
(formerly the Belgian Congo)

To the Belgians, in 1911, goes the credit for introducing the Garratt type to Africa, the continent where it really made its nest and where the greatest and the most numerous classes have been found. However, the earliest Congo Garratts were for narrow-gauge systems not connected to the main network, and formed a very modest start to the Garratt's reign in Africa.

The first Garratt in Africa! The huge machines which rode the rails in Africa's heaviest duties were evolved from this quaint little Belgian colonial machine which operated the Mayumbe railway, a very minor byway from the Congo river to the Mayumbe mountain range to the north. St. Leonard

Chemins de Fer Vicinaux du Mayumbe

This little railway, of 60cm gauge, which runs from Boma, near the mouth of the Congo river, north almost to Gabon, had the honour of introducing the Garratt to Africa, with two minute 0—4—0 + 0—4—0 built by the Société Anonyme de Saint-Léonard of Liége in Belgium.

These little engines were probably, among Garratts, those with the most 'narrow gauge' appearance ever built, and had outside plate frames and crank webs extended to form balance weights. The cylinders had slide valves actuated by Walschaerts gear, and steam was supplied from a non-superheated Belpaire boiler sporting a long stovepipe chimney. The cab was open on all four sides above waist level, the roof being supported on four pillars. Fuel was oil.

Following the first four locomotives, Class A, came eleven enlarged engines, Class B, which differed in appearance by the addition of side tanks on the boiler unit. Then, finally, there came four locomotives of Class C and one of Class E. The class C of 1926 were generally similar, but with larger boilers arranged to burn wood, the rear bunker carrying wood rails on top. The final known class was the E, very similar to class C but with slightly modified boiler dimensions, and

Mayumbe's class B added side tanks to the original pure Garratt concept, while various detail differences are apparent.   Société St Léonard

with wood racks above the side tanks. It is not known what comprised class D, possibly a non-articulated type for shunting.

These little engines probably survived to the end of steam on this railway, dieselisation taking place about 1960, although it is possible that some of these mini-Garratts may still be rusting away at Boma today. Construction details are:

Mayumbe Nos	St Léonard Nos	Date built
1A—2A	1708-09	1911
3A—4A	1715-16	1911
1B—2B	1899-1900	1919
3B—6B	1953-56	1921
7B—11B	2021-25	1924
1C—4C	2056-59	1926
1E	2096	1927

As various batches were added to Mayumbe's roster, experience gained suggested improvements, and the C class had a rack for additional wood fuel, plus spark arresting chimney.   Société St Léonard

Compagnie du Chemins de Fer du Congo

This railway, of 750mm gauge, ran on the south side of the Congo river, from Matadi, more or less opposite Boma, to Leopoldville, higher up the river, by-passing the Congo rapids, which are not navigable.

The 0—6—0 + 0—6—0 Garratts built for this line were generally similar to the Mayumbe engines in appearance, although of course larger, while the first engine of all was an interesting if unsuccessful experiment. Arranged to burn oil, the boiler barrel had slung underneath it two corrugated flues which, at their leading ends, contained the burners, the trailing ends discharging into the firebox, which simply became the combustion chamber. From this the gases passed through the barrel, which was equipped with Servé ribbed tubes, into the smokebox in the normal manner,

(above) Mayumbe's final development placed extra wood atop the side tanks, in class E. To what extent the earlier locomotives were brought into line with the later now seems impossible to determine.   Société St Léonard

(below) The original CF Congo Garratt No 101. Note the burner flues slung underneath the boiler, and fuel tank mounted on the front unit, to suit the forward burner position.   Société St Léonard

(below) The second group of Congo Garratts, with normal Belpaire boiler, arranged for coal burning. Société St Léonard

The third group of Congo Garratts, with modified bunker and pipework.   Société St Léonard

no superheater being provided. Steam was collected in the dome, and fed from it to the cylinders through outside steam pipes. The cylinders, it is believed, had slide valves, while a distinctive feature was the front tank, which was cylindrical.

In service, this engine was a failure as far as its unconventional boiler was concerned, and it was eventually converted to a normal type.

In this form the engine performed well, and in 1919 a further batch of twelve engine was supplied, this time having superheaters, saturated steam from the dome passing to the smokebox header via an external pipe. Outside admission piston valves were fitted, together with a normal rectangular front tank, while they were arranged for coal burning. Nine similar engines followed in 1924.

Finally, ten more engines, slightly heavier and arranged to burn oil, were supplied in 1925, having an oval section rear tank. These Garratts hauled the traffic between Matadi and Leopoldville until after the second world war, when the line was converted to 3ft 6in-gauge and subsequently dieselised.

Building data are:

CF Congo Nos	St Léonard Nos	Date
111	1744	1911
112-23	1901-12	1919
124-32	2001-09	1924
133-42	2040-49	1925

Chemins de Fer du Bas Congo á Katanga

The only Garratts to operate on this railway were twelve built by Forges Usines et Fonderies de et á Haine-St-Pierre in Belgium, to the same design as those supplied two years earlier to Mozambique. The only difference of any significance was that oil was the fuel instead of coal. As these engines operate on the Compagnie des Chemins de fer Katanga-Dilolo-Leopoldville, which is operated by the BCK, they carry the initials KDL. As a matter of interest, this railway has not reached Leopoldville, but runs only to Port Francqui, from whence traffic is shipped down the rivers Kasai and Congo.

The twelve engines, numbered 901—12, were Haine-St Pierre numbers 2097—2108 dated 1953 and are long out of service.

The final batch of Congo Garratts, with oval rear tank for oil fuel.   Société St Léonard

Lettered 'MR' (Mashonaland Railway) Rhodesian 13th class No 165 was photographed at work on a ballast train. Rhodesia Railways

Zimbabwe (formerly Southern Rhodesia) Zambia (formerly Northern Rhodesia)

The name Rhodesia has now disappeared from the World's atlases, thus (as tends to be the fashion) dishonouring the man who welded the former tribal territories, often disputed, to the boundaries now internationally recognised. This has relevance to the railway, and the Garratt, story, inasmuch that all the Garratts in these territories were ordered by Rhodesia Railways, which then administered and operated the railways now within Zimbabwe and Zambia. Various railways combined to form Rhodesia Railways, and these, with their origins, are well documented in Anthony Croxton's book *Railways of Rhodesia*. In early Garratt days, the only traces of the older organisations were on a few locomotives lettered RRM, denoting the Mashonaland section of the railway. This served the eastern areas of the country, lands of the Shona tribe, and should, strictly speaking be written maShona.

Until 1964, Rhodesia Railways served the two territories of Northern and Southern Rhodesia, but in that year, Northern Rhodesia became the Republic of Zambia, and while RR continued as the unitary system for a while, the lines north of the Zambesi eventually became Zambian Railways. From the time of the Unilateral Declaration of Independence in 1965, Southern Rhodesia became, simply, Rhodesia, and the railways remained RR. After the independence elections of 1979, Rhodesia became Zimbabwe-Rhodesia, and at least one Garratt carried new number plates lettered ZRR. From 1980 after the internationally recognised independence, the name 'Rhodesia' has been dropped, and the railways are now the National Railways of Zimbabwe.

The RR entered the field of Garratt operation with a bang in 1926, ordering twelve 2—6—2 + 2—6—2 engines at a time when most railways started with a single experimental Garratt.

These first Garratts, the 13th class, were plate-framed jobs with piston valves, the last two having Lentz poppet-valve cylinders, fed with superheated steam from a Belpaire boiler. Otherwise, they were generally similar to, if slightly larger than, the SAR GD class, introduced the previous year and upon which the design was undoubtedly based.

These engines were placed in service on the difficult Beira Railway route from Vila Machado,

*A rare combination on the West Nicholson branch —
14th class No 504 pilots a 14A on Mulungwane bank,
with a limestone train.*   F. C. Butcher

on Portuguese territory, to Umtali, just inside the Rhodesian border. This route traverses the Amatongas mountain range by means of 1 in 38 gradients and 5 chain curves, reaching an altitude of 3367ft at Umtali. The 13th class remained on this section until 1949, when the line was sold to the CFM, and the Garratts dispersed to Salisbury from where they worked on branch lines until scrapped in 1958. Two engines, Nos 162–3, had previously, in 1939, been sold to the Rhokana Corporation in Northern Rhodesia, where they worked copper trains from the shaft at Mindola to the plant at Nkana. One of these two ended its life spectacularly by colliding with a lorry load of dynamite!

Plate frames were a weakness with the 13th class, hence in 1928 an improved version, the 14th class, was supplied, having bar frames and a round-top boiler, but otherwise of generally similar dimensions. These were also allocated to the Beira line, and eight of them were sold, with it, to the CFM in 1949, the remainder being retained at Salisbury for shunting and branch-line working. During the early 1970s, the

Salisbury area was fully dieselised, and the 14th class concentrated at Bulawayo, for shunting. As dieselisation expanded, they were replaced by newer Garratts, and by 1975 were, to all appearances, finished. Then, in 1979, after four years out of service, the high price and unavailability of oil caused a rethink in motive power policy, and three 14th class were returned to service for shunting at Bulawayo, followed by two more in 1980. No 500 is preserved, and 502/04 were sold for scrap late 1980.

For the even heavier duties from Wankie to Dett and Livingstone, the 16th class was supplied in 1929, these being 2–8–2 + 2–8–2 Garratts having similar features to the 14th class but, of course, being larger all round. Eight were built initially, plus a further dozen in 1938. The addition of this latter batch enabled their duties to be extended down to Umtali, and eventually most of the class migrated to the Salisbury-Umtali line.

With the onset of dieselisation in the early 1960s these useful engines, capable of hauling 700 tons over 1 in 40 gradients, became largely

Two of the original 15th class, with very streamlined front tanks, double-head the Royal train en route for Victoria Falls, in 1947. Rhodesia Railways

redundant, and in 1963—4 nine were sold to the Benguela Railway in Angola, and seven to Dunn's Locomotive Works at Witbank, South Africa, from where they were resold to collieries. By the time they were disposed of, ever more onerous duties, coupled with easing of axle load restrictions, caused many RR Garratts to require additional coal and water supplies, and the 16th class were among those altered to provide an additional 550 gallons of water and 2¼ tons of coal, increasing the total weight by 5 tons. Only two 16th class were not sold for further use, one being scrapped after an accident, while the prototype is now in the railway museum at Bulawayo.

Up to this time, the Garratt had been considered simply as a slow, hard-slogging tractor for heavy gradients, but the smooth running of even these small-wheel types led to the realisation that a larger-wheeled Garratt would be an ideal main-line locomotive. Thoughts at first turned to a double Pacific using the same boiler and other details as the 16th class but, possibly influenced by the Sudan locomotives, Major M. P. Sells, the

CME, extended the conception to a 4—6—4 + 4—6—4, thus enabling more coal and water to be accommodated.

Four of these new 15th class were ordered at first, and were intended for the line from Bulawayo to Mafeking, a route which for most of its distance is within Botswana, formerly known as Bechuanaland.

Apart from the wheel arrangement, the principal difference between these engines and the 16th class was in the front tank which introduced for the first time the 'streamlined' style later adopted by Beyer Peacock for other Garratts on Rhodesian and other railways. The rear tank and bunker of these initial four engines remained of conventional shape, a feature by which they are easily distinguished today.

Initially, they were barred from using their intended route, as the second world war delayed some necessary bridge strengthening, and they were used from Salisbury to Gwelo, their duties including the haulage of the 'Rhodesia Express'. The performances put out by these first four 15th class were quite astounding in terms of avail-

155

Second series 15th class with high front tank, No 360, leaves Victoria Falls on a cool, sunny morning.
F. C. Butcher

Thoroughly Africa — 15A No 417 with standard tank, is framed between two Baobab trees on the climb from the bridge to Victoria Falls station.   Christine Durrant

ability, and for their first six years of life they averaged nearly 6,000 miles per month, including all repair times. When it is considered that this was run on a 3ft 6in-gauge, single-track railway, on a mixture of services, and not on a multi-track, water-level main line, the record stands out as being all the more creditable. Later examples improved upon even this, attaining monthly mileages of up to 10,000.

The success of the original 15th class led to thirty more being built, in two slightly different variations. The second series of ten engines had a high front tank, some 9in higher than the first series, and with square front corners. The rear bunker was of completely radiussed side view, to

match, but coal and water capacities were as before. The final batch of twenty had front tanks of similar contours to the first batch, but with the square corners of the second. Larger capacity bunkers (12½ instead of 10 tons) were fitted, with yet a third side profile, curved at the top but straight backed. The third series front tank became standard, and was fitted to 352 and 353 of the first series, and several of the second series.

Following the third series 15th class were forty engines of class 15A, of the same external appear-

(right) Sold in to South African mine service, RR 16th class 16A is hard at work on the Enyati Railway.   A. E. Durrant

16A class No 626 leaves Heany Junction with a West Nicholson branch train, while a 15A rolls in on a freight from Bulawayo to Gwelo, 1979. A. E. Durrant

ance as the third series 15th, but with boiler pressure increased to 200psi, the total of these useful machines then being seventy-four, making them the most numerous and generally useful locomotives on RR. Apart from the variations mentioned above, several other differences occurred from time to time, for example, one or two boilers were fitted with thermic syphons which were neither removed nor repeated. In the late 1960s, two were fitted with Giesl ejectors in the smokebox and one of these engines also had a superheat booster. The boilers so equipped, circulated within the class, as is normal repair practice on standardised locomotives, and they appeared on engines 380, 381, 382, and 419 at different times. Incidentally, boilers are exchanged freely between 15th, 15A, and 16A classes, and it is no longer possible to distinguish 15th and 15A classes by engine number. For example, in February 1974, eight former 15A were running as 15th class, while nineteen former 15ths were upgraded to 15A. Where a 15th/15A has a boiler previously used on a 16A class, this can be distinguished on the right side of the smokebox by a patch where, on a 16A, the main steam pipe to the rear unit emerges.

While the Giesl ejectors gave good results, the imposition of sanctions on Rhodesia prevented further engines being converted, but in 1970, No 376 was fitted with a locally designed six-jet blast pipe (known as a 'pepper pot'), exhausting through a 20th class chimney. This also gave excellent results which, according to engineers in Bulawayo, are nearly as good as a Giesl ejector properly adjusted, and far better than a mal-adjusted ejector; the adjustable slides on a Giesl ejector were a weak feature, encouraging unauthorised tinkering in running sheds. As a result, all operating 15th/15A locomotives in Zimbabwe now have pepper pot blastpipes.

From an operating point of view, the 15th/15A classes have been so universally useful as to have seen service on all the principal main lines; Bulawayo-Salisbury, Gwelo-Malvernia, Bulawayo-Mafeking, and Bulawayo-Victoria Falls, plus a few north of the Zambesi. Until dieselisation in 1973 they virtually monopolised the Mafeking line, working with two crews on a caboose system, running 968 miles (1550km) round trips and traversing three countries (Rhodesia, Botswana, and South Africa) in the process, a possibly unique steam locomotive working arrangement. Today they may be found working from Bulawayo to Victoria Falls, Gwelo,

158

(above)   A Sunday afternoon regular on the
Pietermaritzburg — Donnybrook line utilised branch
line Garratts returning from washout at Mason's Mill
shed. The GCA plus GF combination shown was
perhaps the most typical.   A. E. Durrant

(below)   Clydesdale Colliery's industrial type 2—6—2
+ 2—6—2 Garratt, ex-works from overhaul, heaves a
load through a bucolic setting of wildflowers and
maizefields, en route to the SAR interchange sidings
at Bezuidenhoutsrust. The Africans on the front
double up as shunters and sanding gear!
A. E. Durrant

(above) Having worn out a couple of GCAs and a Rhodesian 16, Vryheid Coronation Colliery advanced to SAR GEA Garratts, with No 5 shown here resplendent in new blue livery.   A. E. Durrant

(below)   At the 'Nek' on Enyati Railway, loads are assembled from two mines and conveyed to the SAR at Boomlager. Ex-RR 16th class No 618 in unaccustomed maroon livery is about to lead a train which will be banked by the GF in the foreground. The third locomotive in the picture is a Baldwin 2—10—0 rebuilt from a 2—10—2T.   A. E. Durrant

*Ex Sudan double 4—6—4 Garratt, RR class 17, on
shunting duties in Bulawayo.*   F. C. Butcher

and sometimes to West Nicholson, on everything
from mail trains to shunting — a truly mixed
traffic 'maid of all work'. They are included in the
steam rehabilitation programme to be mentioned
later.

The post-war upsurge in traffic created a
motive power demand not easily met, and two
second-hand classes were used to help out while
new power was awaiting its turn on the manufacturers' order books. First, there were the nine
ex-War Department 2—8—2 + 2—8—2s which
were taken into RR stock as the 18th class,
although they were but a short time in Rhodesia,
being sold to the CFM in 1949 together with the
Umtali-Beira line. Details of these will be found in
Chapter 11.

The same year, 1949, in which the 18th and
14th classes were sold to Mozambique, the RR
were able to purchase from the Sudan the class of
ten 4—6—4 + 4—6—4 Garratts, built by Beyer
Peacock in 1937 (see Chapter 7). These were the
forerunners of the 15th class, which they then
supplemented, and they remained in Rhodesia as
the 17th class until 1964—5, when they also were
sold to Mozambique.

The post second world war upsurge of traffic
was felt as much on the branch as on the main
lines, and there was a need for Garratts of similar
capacity to the pre-war 14th and 16th classes. It
was not, however, considered sound policy simply
to repeat the earlier engines, and each was completely re-designed to give improved accessibility
for maintenance and generally increased reliability. Externally, the new designs, classed 14A
and 16A, were recognisable by the 'streamlined'
front tanks and similarly contoured bunker, while
of course such details as Hadfield power reverse

and Beyer Peacock self-adjusting pivots were
incorporated. First built were the thirty engines
of class 16A, followed immediately by the
eighteen 14As. The smaller 14A class remained
wholly in Southern Rhodesia, working various
branch lines, in particular the Fort Victoria,
Selukwe, and Shabani lines out of Gwelo, plus the
mixed trains between Bulawayo and West
Nicholson. The 16A were more widely dispersed,
from Salisbury to the Zambian copperbelt, eleven
of them remaining in Zambia at partition. The
remainder gradually concentrated into the
Bulawayo Gwelo area, on branch line and heavy
shunting work. One of the country's more
spectacular workings was on the West Nicholson
branch, which conveyed limestone from the
quarries at Colleen Bawn to the works at Cement.
It was uphill most of the way, but at Balla Balla,
the grade steepened, and loads were dropped off.
Once a day, a pair of engines would run out from
Bulawayo, pick up the excess loads, and double
head to the factory, making a magnificent sight
and sound as they climbed through the wild gorge
to Mulungwane. When Cabora Bassa dam was
under construction there was a heavy demand for
cement, with sometimes two double-headers
daily, but today such working is rare. Hopefully,
if the wilder political element can be curbed, and
Zimbabwe returns to prosperity, traffic will again
rise so that various combinations of 14A and
16A will again climb Mulungwange. Both classes
are included in the rehabilitation programme.

Finally, we come to Rhodesia's ultimate
Garratt class, the magnificent 20th and 20A
classes of 4—8—2 + 2—8—4 which, apart from
having a larger wheel arrangement than previous
RR Garratts, were also built to a higher axle load,

Midwinter at Wankie can be chilly for the first hour of daylight. A 20th class Garratt leaves a lovely steam trail round the horseshoe curve as it heads the 07.30 mixed from Thomson Junction to Bulawayo, in 1978.   A. E. Durrant

made possible by re-laying the main lines with 80lb rail.

The all-up weight of the 20s is greater than that of South Africa's GL class, but this is partly accounted for by greater coal and water capacities, and the 20s are, in overall size and power capacity, more in line with SAR's GM series.

Technically, they embodied most of the modern practices incorporated in the later Garratts, and were mounted on bar frames with piston-valve cylinders having Walschaerts distribution. The superheated boiler had a round-top firebox with arch tubes, and was mechanically stoked, the first and only Rhodesian class to depart from hand firing. Naturally, Hadfield power reverse and Beyer Peacock self-adjusting pivots were included in the design.

Twenty-one 20th class and forty 20A were

built, the only difference being in the inner radial truck wheels which, in the case of the 20A, were reduced to the size of the bogie wheels.

Quite a number of troubles were experienced with the 20s, both in main-frame fractures and in firebox failures. The frame troubles would probably not have occurred had the design included the cast-steel beds supplied to the contemporary SAR GMA/M classes, while the boilers, being almost identical to those SAR classes, should not have given trouble.

Though they are the most powerful locomotives on the RR, being easily capable of handling 1400 short tons over the 1 in 64½ compensated gradients of the Kafue-Broken Hill line, the 20s have had a relatively unhappy life. Following their initial troubles, and after the former territory of Northern Rhodesia became Zambia, they had to contend with inadequate main-

162

Returned to service in 1980! Zambian Railways class 20A Garratt No 728 approaches Victoria Falls with a southbound freight. For several years ZR has been fully dieselised, but the World oil crisis had prompted a partial return to steam traction. R. Dickinson

tenance, most of the class being allocated to that section for working the coal traffic from the Wankie coalfields up to the copper belt. Furthermore, both the first and last engines, Nos 700 and 760, were scrapped due to extensive damage in collisions, after very short lives.

Nevertheless, mechanical troubles apart, the 20s have proved excellent traffic machines, and the arrival of the first fifteen soon cleared a bottleneck on the Kafue-Lusaka line, while their high haulage capacity largely stopped the proposal to electrify the Bulawayo-Salisbury and Kafue-Nkana lines from being implemented. At the time of partition, only fourteen 20th/20A

remained in Southern Rhodesia, although as Zambia dieselised, another four were acquired by the South. After curing their early troubles, these eighteen engines have been a particularly effective batch of motive power, and have handled much of the coal traffic from Wankie, south to Bulawayo, or north to Victoria Falls, while also putting in appearances on the Gwelo line. These fine locomotives are also very much in the rehabilitation programme for steam, which will now be covered.

Building and numbering details of the Rhodesian Garratts are tabulated below:

Class	Type	First Nos	Second Nos	Builder	Works Nos/Date
13	2-6-2 + 2-6-2	160-171	—	BP	6269-80/26
14	2-6-2 + 2-6-2	215-220	—	BP	6510-15/28
,,	,, ,,	231-232	—	BP	6616-17/29
,,	,, ,,	233-240	500-07	BP	6618-25/29
14A	,, ,,	508-519	—	BP	7581-92/53
15	4-6-4 + 4-6-4	271-274	350-53	BP	6936-39/39
,,	,, ,,	275-280	354-59	BP	7228-33/47
,,	,, ,,	290-293	360-63	BP	7234-37/47
,,	,, ,,	364-383	—	BP	7260-79/48
15A	,, ,,	384-398	—	BP	7326-40/49-50
,,	,, ,,	399-413**	—	BP	7351-65/51
,,	,, ,,	414-423	—	FR-B	2963-72*/52
16	2-8-2 + 2-8-2	221-228	600-07	BP	6562-69/29
,,	,, ,,	259-264	608-13	BP	6877-82/37
,,	,, ,,	265-270	614-19	BP	6899-904/37
16A	,, ,,	620-649	—	BP	7498-527/52-3
17	4-6-4 + 4-6-4	271-280	—	(ex Sudan)	
18	2-8-2 + 2-8-2	281-289	—	(ex WD)	
20	4-8-2 + 2-8-4	700-714	—	BP	7685-99/54
20/20A	,, ,,	715-760	—	BP	7780-825/54

*Sub-let from Beyer Peacock, Nos 7555-64. See also renumbering details in following pages by National Railways of Zimbabwe.
**No 404 renumbered 424

Garratts being rebuilt — in 1980! The production line at RESCCO'S works, Bulawayo, where NRZ Garratts are being extensively renovated for use into the 1990s, reversing a previous policy of dieselisation.
Alan Harris, courtesy RESCCO

A new phase — back to steam

As happened on most railways in the World, Rhodesia was seduced into buying diesel locomotives, with half a dozen shunters plus the first main line diesels in 1955, following the final new steam locomotives. Dieselisation tended to spread from the eastern ends of the country, adjacent to the ports of Beira and Lourenço Marques, through which oil was inexpensively shipped, while the western sections, closer to the enormous coal deposits at Wankie, remained faithful to steam. Cheap oil, plus the lack of a commercial supplier for new steam locomotives, encouraged further dieselisation, and a D-date of 1980 was set.

However, the world oil crisis changed all that! The price of oil was rocketing, and its very availability was ever in doubt, so in 1978 the eminently sensible decision to abandon and

reverse the diesel policy was made. A programme was planned to rebuild completely eighty-seven Garratts for extended use into the 1990s, and to electrify the main line from Salisbury to Gwelo. The local construction of new steam locomotives was proposed by the mechanical branch, but unfortunately this was not implemented, although with the high capital costs of electrification, new steam locomotives of advanced design would have been a more economical proposition. Some idea of the possible capacity of a new Garratt design, with a 20 ton axle-load, to suit RR's existing main line track of 91lb/yd was given in a paper presented by the author to the Institution of Mechanical Engineers in Bulawayo, in 1979.

The engines selected for rebuilding are from classes 14A, 15th/15A, 16A, and 20th/20A, and as the capacity of Bulawayo workshops was insufficient for a major venture of this kind, the project was co-ordinated jointly with various local private firms. The main stripping down and re-erection of the locomotives is being carried out by RESSCO, a steel construction firm who set up a locomotive division for the purpose, while Boiler and Steam Services overhaul the boilers and fit new inner fireboxes (manufactured by RESSCO), where necessary. All locomotives are being fitted with roller bearings on driving and coupled axles, with cannonboxes cast and machined by Issels & Son. Where tanks and bunkers require renewal, the 14A and 16A are being fitted with new assemblies of increased capacity.

To tide the railway over the motive power shortage while rebuilding is carried out, five old 14th class have been reinstated for shunting at Bulawayo, and 21 class GMAM Garratts hired from SAR. The GMAM are dimensionally very similar to the native 20s, and it has been very interesting to compare the performance of two designs having almost identical boilers, tractive effort, and bunker capacities. For reasons yet undetermined, the SAR Garratts have proved very heavy on coal, and despite having bunker capacities increased by about two tons, by raised side sheets, are given lower load ratings (for example, Thomson Junction to Dett, 1300 tons GMAM, 1640 tons 20th) not through any deficiency in the engine's power capacity, but simply to prevent it running out of coal. The SAR numberplates were removed, because armour-plating was fitted to the cabsides in case of terrorist activity during the war in Rhodesia in the last years before legal independence in 1980. These locomotives are now reverting to normal, following the official end of the war.

While the GMAM are holding the fort, mainly from Bulawayo to Thomson Junction, although also to Gwelo, the rebuilt Garratts are being turned out, the programme being about 40 per cent complete at the time of writing, perhaps 60 per cent complete by the time this book is published. The larger engines are being given attractive names of Matabele origin, the 15s being named after animals and birds, and the 20s after rivers and Matabele regiments. A partial renumbering is also in hand.

National Railways of Zimbabwe — naming and renumbering of Garratts

By 1980, NRZ had become unique in several ways. It was the first major railway in the world to institute a motive power policy change, to suit the world oil crisis, which involved the replacement of diesels by steam, but it backed up this policy by spending substantial sums of money in rehabilitating its steam power with extensive

rebuilding, including the provision of roller bearings, and other improvements, recognising that the remaining 'straight' locomotives were limited in capacity, they were withdrawn and sold for scrap, apart from a few retained at the museum for special trains, and further Garratts were hired from SAR. As a result, NRZ has become the first and only railway in the world where every operable steam locomotive — goods, passenger, or shunting, is a Garratt!

As many of the RR 16A, 20th, and 20A class locomotives are in Zambia, it was decided to close up the number gaps in Zimbabwe by renumbering these classes, while as the only difference between the 15th and 15A classes is the boiler pressure, often changing after overhaul and boiler exchange, the class designation '15A' has been discarded. Renumbering details are:—

Class 16A. New numbers 601—15, formerly 625/6/8/9/31/2/3/5/6/7/8/43/5/7/8. Three 16As were on loan to Mozambique when the border was closed, and they are currently (1980) exiled on the Beira line. If and when returned to NRZ, they will receive new numbers 616—18, formerly RR 627/34/39. Paradoxically, while the former RR initials on tank and bunker sides are being removed, and replaced by new NRZ number-plates, the three 16As, currently running in a foreign country, could be the last running with the RR insignia. At the time of writing, traffic between the border and Umtali, on the newly re-opened rail link, has been noted behind an ex-RR 16A, rather than a local Garratt. However, eight SAR GMAMs have been hired to Mozambique as from late 1980, and these may well release the 16As for return to NRZ.

Class 20. New numbers 730—37, formerly 705/7/9/10/4/6/7/8.

Class 20A. New numbers 740—50, formerly 723/4/6/7/9/38/45/7/9/8/50 (in that order).

Naming of locomotives

The 15 and 20 classes of locomotives are being named as they pass through RESCCO's works, the names chosen being attractive ones of local origin in Sindibele, language of the Matabele, through whose tribal areas the main line steam largely operates. The 15th class are being given names of birds and animals, the 20th class of Matabele regiments, and the 20A class of local rivers. The only exception is 20A No 747 which will retain its old number and be called *Jumbo*. As 15th No 420 is called *Indlovu*, there will thus be two elephants in the fleet! Apart from 747, names have not been allocated to individual engines, so that enthusiasts will have a happy time discovering which locomotive has what name! The names allocated (with the English renderings), with engine numbers where known, are:

Garratt rehabilitation programme — as at June 1981

Loco numbers Old	New	Nameplate	English Meaning	Date ex-RESCCO Actual
643	612	—	—	7.6.79
636	609	—	—	29.6.79
625	601	—	—	11.7.79
420	—	Indhlovu	Elephant	6.8.79
419	—	Isambane	Ant Bear	3.9.79
514	—	—	—	21.9.79
632	606	—	—	9.10.79
519	—	—	—	30.10.79
645	613	—	—	19.11.79
511	—	—	—	22.11.79
515	—	—	—	21.12.79
520	—	—	—	23.1.80
633	607	—	—	12.2.80
629	604	—	—	3.3.80
522	—	—	—	20.3.80
631	605	—	—	31.3.80
628	603	—	—	26.4.80
635	608	—	—	14.5.80
726	742	Gwaai	—	17.5.80
523	—	—	—	24.5.80
626	602	—	—	6.6.80
525	—	—	—	16.6.80
512	—	—	—	12.7.80
637	610	—	—	15.7.80
638	611	—	—	22.7.80
517	—	—	—	31.7.80
510	—	—	—	14.8.80
422	—	Inkonikoni	Wildebeest (Gnu)	3.9.80
647	614	—	—	13.9.80
508	—	—	—	26.9.80
718	737	Ingubu	—	4.10.80
648	615	—	—	13.10.80
521	—	—	—	27.10.80
385	—	Ingwenya	Crocodile	13.12.80
391	—	Ingugama	Gemsbok (Oryx)	21.1.81
421	—	Intundhla	Giraffe	30.1.81
397	—	Inyathi	Buffalo	9.2.81
382	—	Iganyana	Wild Dog	26.2.81
402	—	Impofu	Eland	7.3.81
710	733	Imbizo	—	27.3.81
387	—	Imvubu	Hippopotamus	31.3.81
518	—	—	—	24.4.81
513	—	—	—	7.5.81
392	—	Ithaka	Roan Antelope	15.5.81
407	—	Ukhozi	Eagle	30.5.81
409	—	Inkhakha	Pangolin	15.6.81
404*	424	Isilwana	Lion	late.6.81

* was formerly 404

Scheduled

Old	New	Nameplate	English Meaning	Actual
705	730	—	—	8.81
410	—	—	—	7.81
415	—	—	—	7.81
394	—	—	—	7.81
524	—	—	—	8.81
414	—	—	—	8.81
386	—	—	—	8.81
396	—	—	—	8.81
406	—	—	—	9.81
381	—	—	—	9.81
423	—	—	—	9.81
380	—	—	—	10.81
371	—	—	—	10.81
376	—	—	—	10.81
377	—	—	—	10.81
372	—	—	—	11.81
370	—	—	—	11.81
400	—	—	—	11.81
n/d	—	—	—	12.81
n/d	—	—	—	12.81
n/d	—	—	—	1.82
n/d	—	—	—	1.82

(n/d=not yet decided)

Old	New	Nameplate	English Meaning	Actual
727	743	—	—	3.82
729	744	—	—	3.82
714	734	—	—	3.82
756	750	—	—	4.82
717	736	—	—	4.82
738	745	—	—	4.82
753	748	—	—	6.82
723	740	—	—	6.82
747	—	Jumbo	—	7.82
709	732	—	—	7.82
707	731	—	—	7.82
724	741	—	—	7.82
716	735	—	—	9.82
746	—	—	—	10.82
749	—	—	—	10.82
509	—	—	—	8.82
516	—	—	—	9.82

Names not yet allocated

15th class

Inkolongwane	Hartebeest
Igogo	Klipspringer
Ingwe	Leopard
Inungu	Porcupine
Imbila	Rock Rabbit
Umayelane	Spring Hare
Ubhejane	Black Rhino
Umkhombo	White Rhino
Inkolome	Tsessebe
Ingulungdundu	Bush Pig
Isidumuka	Water Buck
Idube	Zebra
Umziki	Reed Buck
Umtshwayeli	Sable Antelope
Ibhalabhala	Kudu
Umzwazwa	Brown Hawk
Umahelwane	Black Goshawk
Itsheme	Great Bustard
Ikolo	Hornbill
Umathebene	Kestrel
Udwai	Secretary Bird

20th class
Ihlathi
Insuga
Amaveni
Isiziba
Induba
Enxa

20A class
Shangani
Bembezi
Bubi
Insiza
Lukozi
Umzingwane
Tuli
Umguza
Ingwezi

Zambia Railways

The oil crisis has also affected Zambia, and it is expected that a similar rebuilding scheme may take place, as in Zimbabwe. Already, one or two 20th class Garratts have been returned to service, in their original condition, but the proposals being considered include roller bearings not only to the axleboxes, but also to coupling and connecting rods. It is hoped to use Zambian coal, which is not particularly good, but now that more normal relations are enjoyed between Zambia and Zimbabwe, the better Wankie coal could be used.

Angola

Angola, the former Portuguese colony on the west coast of Africa, is typical of colonial possessions in having its railway system entirely orientated to the purpose of conveying raw material and products between the coast and the interior. Of the four railway systems, which are not physically connected, three are of 3ft 6in gauge, and each used Garratts. Despite the various builders concerned, and the range of dates over which the locomotives were constructed, all are of the 4—8—2 + 2—8—4 type.

Poppet valves and wood burning — a rare Garratt species, especially in 1974. Benguela class 10a¹ No 305 prepares for duty in the yard at Nova Lisboa (now Huambo). A. E. Durrant

Benguela Railway (Caminhos de Ferro Benguela)

The Benguela (formerly spelt Benguella) Railway was a remarkable concern, stretching 1346km from the coast at Lobito Bay to the Belgian Congo (Zaïre) border, and taking 23 years to complete, although for eleven years from 1913 to 1924, no progress was made. Katanga copper was the traffic sought after, hence for the whole of this lengthy construction period, the undeveloped lands of Angola provided little in the way of local traffic. Thus, for the first twenty years, traffic was handled by ten 6th class 4—6—0s, half a dozen assorted 4—8—0s, and four 0—6—2T rack engines for the climb up the coastal escarpment. Connection through to the Congo required an immediate increase in motive power, and Beyer Peacock supplied six large 4—8—2 + 2—8—4 Garratts in 1927, of advanced design with Lentz poppet valves actuated by Walschaerts gear. The units had plate frames, and Belpaire fireboxes were fired with wood. The CFB was remarkable in being a railway which grew its own fuel, having large estates of eucalyptus trees cultivated mainly for locomotive fuel!

These Garratts were able to haul 450 ton trains over 1 in 40 gradients, and as traffic movers were a great success. However, several mechanical improvements were possible, and fourteen further Garratts built in 1929 had bar frames, and piston valves, while extended piston rods drove on to the third coupled axle of each unit, compared with the second axle of the original batch. The railway thus had twenty high capacity Garratts, which sufficed for the depression and second world war years, although things must have been fairly tight during the war.

After the war, further Garratts were required, and eighteen more were built in 1951—52. The same basic dimensions were retained, but further improvements were incorporated, improved cylinders with straight ports and long lap valves, plus SKF roller bearings on the bogie axles. Externally, they were distinguished by the post-war 'streamlined' front tanks. While in course of delivery, a further ten of these locomotives were ordered, differing by the use of oil fuel, and at a later date, a few of the third batch were altered to oil firing. By 1955—56, the railway thus possessed 48 Garratts of the same basic design, but incorporating successive design improvements.

After 1960, yet more Garratts were needed to cope with increasing traffic, but by then commercial builders were unable to supply, and it was fortunate that Rhodesia Railways had nine surplus 16th class 2—8—2 + 2—8—2 Garratts, having the same basic cylinder and wheel dimensions as the CFB Garratts, but with slightly smaller boilers, and, designed for coal firing, considerably less fuel capacity. Nevertheless, these were a most welcome addition to the available motive power fleet, and tended to be used on the section of line closest to the Zaïre border.

Several modifications were made to CFB Garratts. All, or most, were fitted with single Kylchap exhausts, and in 1962 two, 343 and 366, were equipped with Giesl ejectors. No 343, burning wood, showed a 12·4 per cent fuel economy compared with the Kylchap control locomotive, despite which no further Giesl units were ordered. The latest Garratts were fitted with Beyer Peacock's patent self-adjusting pivots, and so successful did these prove that the remaining older Garratts were also so fitted, the pivots being manufactured in the railway's workshops at Nova Lisboa (formerly, and now again, Huambo), where locomotive overhauls were or are carried out. The Garratts were used over the whole line from Benguela to the border, the short coastal section from Lobito Bay to Benguela being almost entirely in the hands of unarticu-

167

(above) A 'dupla' leaves a station on the Benguela Railway, with second series Garratt No 322 leading, and another Garratt cut in midway, the whole nicely framed by an indigenous tree.   F. C. Butcher

(below) Third series CFB Garratt 343, with streamlined tank and wood firing, takes on additional fuel at a wayside loop in central Angola. F. C. Butcher

Engine change at Benguela. Fourth series Garratt 364, oil fired, about to cut off the main line passenger train it has just brought down the escarpment. The 4—8—2 on the left will haul the train along the coastal stretch to Lobito Bay terminus.   A. E. Durrant

lated locomotives which, incidentally, burned imported coal, the railway thus using coal, oil, and wood simultaneously on different sections. For about forty years there was also a short rack section, about 2km long, through the Lengue gorge, but this was replaced by an adhesion diversion about 1950. From about 1975, this in turn was replaced by the 'Cubal variant' route from Catumbela to Cubal, a much easier route, diesel operated from the outset, so that Garratt working was restricted to the upcountry sections inland from Cubal.

In later years, train working on the CFB was an exciting experience, with most trains needing two locomotives, the second being cut into the middle of the train, a mode of working known locally as a 'dupla'. Many duplas were operated by two Garratts, while others had combinations of unarticulated and Garratt power. Freight trains were usually of a very international character, with South African, Rhodesian, Congolese and local wagons seen regularly. From 1976 the country attained nominal 'independence', which has meant the replacement of the Portuguese colonists by Cuban military occupation. Southern

Angola, including the CFB, has been the scene of war between anti-communist guerillas and Cuban invaders, and one of the casualties has been the railway, whose once splendidly maintained Garratts are probably all rusting hulks today.

Building details are as follows:

Class	CFB Nos	Beyer Peacock Nos	Date
10aI	301-306	6333-38	1927
10aII	311-324	6602-15	1929
10aIII	331-333	7366-68	1951
,,	334-342	7369-77	1952
,,	343-348	7593-98	1952
10aIV	361-370	7667-76	1955
	381-389	(ex RR 601/02/07/ 10/11/15/16/17/19)	

Luanda Railway (Caminhos de Ferros Luanda)

This line, now incorporated as the Caminhos de Ferros Angola, and originally of metre gauge, runs, as its title suggests, inland from Luanda, which is the capital city of Angola.

169

*A dupla in action. Standard CFB practice on heavy
loads was to have a second engine cut into the train
midway along. In this case, both are 4th series
Garratts.* C. P. Lewis

The two Garratt classes built for the line were
originally to metre gauge but have now, with the
line, been converted to 3ft 6in. Although the first
section is fairly flat, over the coastal plain,
gradients of up to 1 in 33 are encountered on the
climb inland to the central African plateau.

First were six Beyer Peacock engines supplied
in 1949, to the same development of the wartime
light design as proved so successful elsewhere.
These proved the success of the Garratt type and
in 1954 a further six, to an entirely different
design, were supplied by Krupp. Although of
much the same size, they featured an unusual
tank design, as will be seen from the illustration,
while the boiler was of the round-top type. Bar
frames and normal piston-valve cylinders with
Walschaerts gear completed the ensemble. Like
the earlier engines, they were oil fired.

By 1974, only one or two CFL Garratts

remained in regular use, and one of the Krupp
engines had been transferred to Moçamedes. The
position today is obscure, the Marxist government, in their usual oppressive manner, disallow-
ing visits from innocent railway enthusiasts.

Building data are:

CFL Nos	Builder	Builders' Nos	Date
501-06	BP	7308-13	1949
551-56	Krupp	2493-98	1954

Moçamedes Railway
(Caminhos de Ferro Moçademes)

This railway, the southernmost in Angola,
started in 1905 as a 600mm gauge line from the
port of Moçamedes, across the coastal plain, and

(above) Climbing out of Luanda, a Beyer Peacock Garratt of the Ängolan Railways snakes a long freight round a detour caused by a washout. C. P. Lewis

(below) One of Krupp's unusually styled Garratts heads east out of Luanda on the Angolan Railways.   C. P. Lewis

Henschel 4—8—2 + 2—8—4 No 105 in service, burning oil, on the Moçamedes Railway, Angola. Author's collection

Mozambique

Caminhos de Ferro Moçambique

Railways in the former Portuguese colony of Moçambique have long been users of Garratts, although only in 1949 were any Garratts owned by the CFM.

Trans Zambesia Railway

This line conveyed traffic to and from the port of Beira, leaving the Rhodesian main line at Dondo Junction, and heading generally north across the Zambezi to Nyasaland. For service on this line, in 1924, two 2—6—2 + 2—6—2 Garratts were supplied by Beyer Peacock, to the same design as those for the New Cape Central Railway in South Africa, and differing only in details to suit the railway, the principal variation being in the use of wood fuel, necessitating extension rails to the bunker. The two original engines were joined by a third in 1930, but all three were withdrawn from service in 1947. Later the TZR was split up between the Nyasaland and the Moçambique railways, each buying its respective territorial section. Building data were:

up the escarpment to Sa da Bandeira (now Lubango). Little is known of the early loco-motives, believed to be mainly small Decauville tank engines, with 0—8—2Ts and 0—10—0Ts from Germany added in the 1920s. In 1949 it was decided to broaden the gauge to 3ft 6in and extend further inland, several odd tender engines being acquired from other parts of Angola for construction work. As main traffic machines were bought six 2—8—2s from Jung, plus six 4—8—2 + 2—8—4s Garratts from Henschel, bar framed, piston valve jobs, of quite Beyer Peacock appearance. These carried CFM numbers 101—06, were Henschel 27000—05 dated 1953, and were available for the first 3ft 6in services in 1954. Enormous iron ore deposits were discovered inland, trebling the railway's tonnage from 1967 to 1968, and doubling again by 1971. Further Garratts being unobtainable, the railway became fully dieselised by 1970, although in 1974, all the steam locomotives, including the Garratts, were in store at Sa da Bandeira workshops. It is understood that because of Marxist mismanagement, the whole railway is now out of use, although no confirmation of this is possible.

TZR No	Name	Beyer Peacock No	Date
5	*Sacadura Cabral*	6178	1924
6	*Luiz de Camoes*	6179	1924
7	*Antonio Enes*	6380	1930

The information on names given above was supplied by the Malawi Railways and appear to have changed from those originally carried, the Beyer Peacock records showing Nos 5 and 6 as *Gago Continho* and *Sacadura Cabral* respectively. Under the combined Nyasaland and Trans-Zambezia Railways which eventually operated the three Garratts, they were Class 'E', numbers 16 to 18.

Moçambique Railways

The CFM is a national system comprising the

Trans-Zambesia Railway, now in Mozambique, once used three light Garratts similar to SAR class GC, but arranged as woodburners. Beyer Peacock

Newly repainted in the CFM's grey boilered livery, a former Rhodesian 14th class No 903 poses at Gondola, Mozambique, in 1969.   A. E. Durrant

half-dozen railways, formerly independent, which wend their ways inland from various coastal ports. Of these, the Beira railway is by far the most difficult to work, having 1 in 37 gradients on the climb up to Umtali in Zimbabwe. This line, originally of two-foot gauge, was operated as an integral part of the Rhodesian Railways system until 1949, when it was sold to the CFM.

With the railway came two classes of Garratt, eight 14th class 2—6—2 + 2—6—2s and all nine of

the 18th class 2—8—2 + 2—8—2, the latter being of course ex-War Department engines. The CFM numbered these 901—08 and 981—9 respectively, and they are still nominally at work today.

Further Garratts were soon required, and as a stop-gap measure four South African GF class were bought in 1950, and numbered 911—14. These have had the tanks and bunkers 'streamlined' subsequently, while number 911 has been withdrawn from service.

Passenger train near Beira, Mozambique Railways, headed by former SAR class GF, modified with 'streamlined' front and rear tanks.   A. E. Durrant

Steaming into its third ownership (see also pages 103 and 161), ex Rhodesian and Sudan 4—6—4 + 4—6—4 at Dondo Entroncamento, near Beira. A. E. Durrant

Soon after, Haine St Pierre in Belgium built the CFM's first new Garratts, twelve 4—8—2 + 2—8—4 having the same size wheels and cylinders as the ex-RR 18th class, but otherwise being generally enlarged all round. Surprisingly, they retained the plate-type frame design of the wartime engines and contained the same basic features, such as round-top boilers and piston-valve cylinders. The tanks and bunkers had the 'streamlined' contours, while the cab sides sloped sharply inward at window level. These engines were numbered 951—62, and two were on loan to the Lourenço Marques system in the late 1960s,

traffic on the Beira lines being rather slack due to the sanctions imposed upon Rhodesia.

In 1956, Henschel supplied the CFM's most impressive and modern Garratts, the five 4—8—2 + 2—8—4s numbered 971—5. These were basically an enlargement of the Belgian-built 951 class, but with larger wheels and higher boiler pressure. Cast-steel bed frames were used, with outside bearings on the two-wheel trucks, the design being similar to that of the SAR GMA/M classes, all axles having roller bearings, while spring-loaded wedge horns were included.

The boiler was larger than in previous classes,

Belgian Garratt No 956 rolls through the Amatongas forest on a well maintained stretch of CFM's main line to Umtali. A. E. Durrant

CFM Henschel Garratt No 972 heads through the Amatongas forest with a train bound for Beira in 1969. A. E. Durrant

and included a welded steel inner firebox with two thermic syphons and two arch tubes. Fuel is fed by an HTI mechanical stoker, and at the smokebox end a double Kylchap chimney is included. To round off the design, these imposing locomotives are fitted with smoke deflectors and painted in maroon livery.

To complete the CFM's Garratt roster, the ten 4—6—4 + 4—6—4 Garratts, originally built for Sudan, were purchased from the Rhodesian Railways in 1964 and numbered 921—30. About the same time, three more of the wartime 2—8—2 + 2—8—2s were bought from the Congo Ocean Railway which had dieselised. Building and origin data of this interesting collection of Garratts is appended below, and it might be added that all are allocated to the Beira division, the 911 and 921 classes at Beira for passenger and freight work respectively, and the heavier engines at Gondola, halfway up the main gradient, for all duties between Vila Machado, at the foot of the escarpment, through the Amatongas forest to Gondola, and on to the Zimbabwe border at Machipanda. From time to time, double heading of Garratts, on the Rhodesian system, with several wagons between the engines, was practised, while on at least two occasions some of the 951 class have been loaned to Lourenço Marques, on one occasion for working into Swaziland.

Since the independence of Mozambique, most of the Portuguese inhabitants, who carried out much of the skilled work, fled to Portugal, leaving the Garratts on the Beira line to deteriorate badly. Three RR 16A Garratts were loaned to the CFM, and when the border was closed during the Rhodesian war, they became trapped. Now that the border has reopened, these three Garratts will doubtless be returned to Zimbabwe. Furthermore, reopening of the border has created a sudden locomotive shortage. It is believed that traffic on the lower sections can be handled by unarticulated locomotives transferred from Maputo (formerly Lourenço Marques), but Garratts are needed for the heavy sections. At least one 951 class has arrived at Mafeking with a request that it be overhauled by SAR, but at the time of writing the solution is to hire surplus GMA/M Garratts from South Africa.

CFM Nos	Type	Builder/Builders' Nos	Date
901-908	2-6-2 + 2-6-2	(ex RR Nos 215-220, 231-32)	
911-914	4-6-2 + 2-6-4	(ex SAR Nos 2370, 2419, 2420, 2432)	
921-930	4-6-4 + 4-6-4	(ex RR 271-80, originally SR, see Chapter 7)	
951-962	4-8-2 + 2-8-4	HStP 2059-70	1952
971-975	4-8-2 + 2-8-4	Henschel 28642-46	1956
981-989	2-8-2 + 2-8-2	(ex RR Nos 281-289; ex WD, see Chapter 11)	
990-992	2-8-2 + 2-8-2	(ex Congo Ocean Rly; ex WD, see Chapter 11)	

Class	Type	Cylinders Dia × Stroke (in)	Coupled Wheel Dia (ft in)	Boiler Press (psi)	Tract Effort @ 75% (lb)	Grate Area (sq ft)	Max Dia Boiler (ft in)	Heating Surface (sq ft) Firebox	Tubes	Superheater	Weights in Working Order (Tons) Max Axle	Adhesive	Total	Water Cpcty (Gal)	Fuel Cpcty (Tons/Gal)	Literature Reference	Remarks
CF Mayumbe																	
A	0-4-0 + 0-4-0	7·87×11·81	1-11⅝	178	6900	8·6	3-3	36·6	369·2	Nil	6·4	23·15	23·15	440	172G	W181	
B	0-4-0 + 0-4-0	7·87×11·81	1-11⅝	185	9900	9·7	3-3	47·4	458·5	Nil	6·45	25·4	25·4	736	265G	W181	As built
C	0-4-0 + 0-4-0	7·87×11·81	1-11⅝	185	9900	10·9		47·9	458·3	Nil		26·5	26·5	738	¾t	—	Altered
E	0-4-0 + 0-4-0	7·87×11·81	1-11⅝	185	9900	10·9		46·9	447·8	Nil		29·0	29·0	716		—	
CF Congo																	
111	0-6-0 + 0-6-0	12·2×13·78	2-8⅝	199	18760	Nil	3-10½	123·8	1093·6	Nil	—	54·2	54·2	1014		W191 L225/13	
111	0-6-0 + 0-6-0	12·2×13·78	2-8⅝	199	18760	19·37	4-5⅛	80·7	759·9	116·25	—	54·2	54·2	1014	400G	W191	
112} 124}	0-6-0 + 0-6-0	13·38×13·78	2-8⅝	199	22558	22·6	4-5⅛	86·1	851·4	200·2	9·4	53·9	53·9	661	3t	W191	
133	0-6-0 + 0-6-0	13·38×13·78	2-8⅝	199	22558	22·6	4-5⅛	86·1	851·4	200·2	9·75	58·45	58·45	881	312G	W191	
Bas Congo Katanga																	
900	4-8-2 + 2-8-4	19×24	3-9½	180	51700	57·4	7-0	236	2260	610	13·72	109·8	184·6	5500	10t	—	
Rhodesia Railways																	
13th	2-6-2 + 2-6-2	16×24	4-0	180	34560	38·8	6-0	164·0	1676·0	380	13·0	77·55	122·15	4350	7t	Re May/26	
14th	2-6-2 + 2-6-2	16×24	4-0	180	34560	38·8	6-0	174·0	1676·0	380	13·5	81·0	126·0	3600	7t	L279/26	
14A	2-6-2 + 2-6-2	16×24	4-0	180	34560	38·6	6-0	174·0	1667·0	374	13·6	81·1	131·65	3600	7t	L73/52	
											13·75		181·23		10t	L139/54	
15th	4-6-4 + 4-6-4	17½×26	4-9	180	37720	49·6	6-6	212·0	2110·0	494	15·2	79·5	186·74	7000	12t	L226/40	
15A	4-6-4 + 4-6-4	17½×26	4-9	200	41908	49·6	6-6	212·0	2110·0	494	15·2	79·5	186·74	7000	12t	G127/38	
16th	2-8-2 + 2-8-2	18½×24	4-0	180	46204	49·6	6-6	212·0	2110·0	494	13·8	106·0	155·3	5050	9t	L6/30	
16A	2-8-2 + 2-8-2	18½×24	4-0	200	51338	49·6	6-6	212·0	2110·0	481	14·65	115·65	169·2	5600	8·5t	L184/53	
17th	4-6-4 + 4-6-4	16¾×26	4-9	190	36473	43·2	6-0	184·0	1776·0	440	14·0	83·16	166·1	6900	12·5t		
18th	2-8-2 + 2-8-2	19×24	3-9½	180	51413	51·3	7-0	212·0	2328·0	470	13·2	103·75	151·8	4600	9t	L111/52	
20th	4-8-2 + 2-8-4	20×26	4-3	200	61176	63·1	7-3	233·0	2791·0	748	17·0	136·3	223·4	8000	14t	L31/55	
20A	4-8-2 + 2-8-4	20×26	4-3	200	61176	63·1	7-3	233·0	2791·0	748	17·15	136·3	225·5	8000	14t	L11/59	
Trans Zambezia Railway																	
E	2-6-2 + 2-6-2	15×22	3-6¾	180	31270	33·9		157	1530	271	11	65·75	99·65	3500	Wood 400ft³	L110/24 L211/27	
CF Moçambique																	
951	4-8-2 + 2-8-4	19×24	3-9½	180	51700	57·4	7-0	236	2260	610	13·4	106·75	183·8	5500	10t	L33/56	
971	4-8-2 + 2-8-4	19×24	4-0 ± o	200	54000	61·3	7-3	280	2345·5	873·8	14·55	114·6	194·3	5500	10t		
Benguela Railway																	
10aᴵ	4-8-2 + 2-8-4	18½×24	4-0	180	46200	51·3	6-9	221	2160	467	12·95	102·9	160·6	5000	Wood 540ft³	L138/27	
10aᴵᴵ	4-8-2 + 2-8-4	18½×24	4-0	180	46200	51·3	6-9	229	2320	467	13·2	105·7	171·1	5000	Wood 540ft³	—	
10aᴵᴵᴵ	4-8-2 + 2-8-4	18½×24	4-0	180	46200	51·3	6-9	229	2160	467	13·2	105·6	178·0	5000	Wood 540ft³	L13/53	
10aⱽᴵ	4-8-2 + 2-8-4	18½×24	4-0	180	46200	51·3	6-9	217	2170	418	13·25	105·6	180·3	4800	1600G	—	
Luanda Railway																	
501	4-8-2 + 2-8-4	16×24	4-0	200	38400	48·75	6-0	215	1779	370	11·25	90	149	5500	1500G Oil	L103/49	
551	4-8-2 + 2-8-4	18½×21⅝	3-7±r	200	51000	48·9		253	1726	545	13·0	102·0	163·5	7050	8·85t	—	
Moçamedes Railway																	
101	4-8-2 + 2-8-4	18½×24	4-0	200	46200	51·6		229	2120	645	13·2	105·5	138·8	5000	6t	—	

Chapter 10

East Africa

Kenya, Uganda, Tanzania (formerly Tanganyika)

East Africa was the last of the three African territories which rely on the Garratt to a larger extent than elsewhere, and it is surprising to think that railways in East Africa are almost entirely a twentieth century phenomenon, the first main line, from Mombasa to Nairobi, then spelt Nyrobi, being completed as late as 1899. This was the Uganda Railway, built against strong British parliamentary opposition, to open up trade to Uganda and to assist in abolishing the slave trade.

Much material, including track and rolling stock, was second-hand from India, thus determining the gauge at one metre, and with this material came the construction labour of Indian coolies. The line proceeded under great difficulties, disease and lack of water taking great toll of the coolies, who were also decimated by marauding man-eating lions, bringing construction completely to a standstill on more than one occasion.

After reaching Nyrobi, the line was pushed westwards towards Uganda, and the difficulties here were due more to the terrain than anything else, the line having to climb to a summit of over 9000ft before dropping down to the level of Lake Victoria. In order to illustrate this, the composite gradient diagram is shown on page 178 in which the upper line represents the profile from Mombasa to Kampala. To the same horizontal and vertical scale is the main line from Euston to Wick, where such legendary gradients as Shap, Beattock, and Druimuachdar appear as mere pimples compared with the East African main line! Such were the difficulties that beset operation on this newcomer to the railway scene, and which have, as we shall see, caused the railway to be continually developing locomotives of greater power.

While the Kenya-Uganda section is the main part of the system, it is not the senior, this distinction being claimed by the railways in Tanganyika (now Tanzania), then Deutsches Ostafrika or German East Africa. The first section of the Usambarabahn from Tanga to Neu Moschi was opened as far as Pongwe in April 1894, this line reaching Arusha, under the slopes of Mount Kilimanjaro and eventually connecting with the KUR by a link from Kahe to Voi. Of greater importance was the main Tanganjikabahn from the coast at Dar-es-Salaam to Kigoma on Lake Tanganyika. This was a later concern, with construction not commencing until 1905, and in neither of these lines were severe conditions of climate, fauna, or gradients encountered as on the KUR.

Turning now to motive power, the Uganda Railway started with a most pathetic bunch of second-hand Indian power — 'A' class 2—4—0T, 'E' class 0—4—2, and 'N' class 2—6—0, none of which could do much more than heave their own weary bodies over the heavy gradients of the railway. The first reasonable power was the class of 0—6—6—0 compound Mallets introduced in 1913 for the heaviest sections, with 4—8—0s built from 1914 sufficing for the easier portions of the line. This venture into articulateds at an early date seems to have put the authorities off such power for a while, the usual sluggishness and poor riding of this type no doubt prevailing.

However, following the successful use of Garratts elsewhere, the KUR in 1926 placed in service the four locomotives comprising Class 'EC'. These were, to a large extent, two of the standard 4—8—0s placed back to back, plus the addition of a 'trailing' truck on each unit, thus making the 4—8—2 + 2—8—4 type the first such constructed. As in the 4—8—0s, plate frames were used and piston-valve cylinders of good design with straight ports were incorporated. All wheels were flanged, and the bogie wheels had disc centres of the type so familiar in India.

The superheated boiler had a Belpaire firebox arranged to burn wood, and with the facility given by the Garratt design the grate area was two and a half times that of the 4—8—0 types. These engines were at first put to work on the Nairobi-Nakuru-Kisumu section which was laid with 50lb track, and on this stretch they were capable of hauling 520 tons on 1 in 50 gradients, compensated, and 457 tons uncompensated. These first four engines, Nos 41—4, had a comparatively short life on the KUR for in August 1939 they, together with Nos 51 and 53 of the later 'EC1' class, were shipped to Indo-China, the six engines being there numbered 201—206. Since then all trace of their fate has been lost, but they have presumably by now been scrapped.

After a two-year trial of the ECs, the KUR decided to go in for Garratts in a big way, and

Longest lived of the early East African Garratts were the North British-built 52 class, represented by 5202 Kavirondo. EAR

apart from half a dozen each of the heavy 2—8—2s and standard 4—8—0s in 1928 and 1930 respectively, nothing but Garratts was delivered to the railway until the end of its separate existence. The 2—8—2s were purchased from Robert Stephensons in 1928 for the Nairobi-Mombasa section, then laid with 80lb rails, and it was the intention that those splendid engines would haul the loads over this section, handing over to the Garratts at Nairobi for the trip up-country over 50lb track. So versatile did the Garratts show themselves to be, however, that it was soon

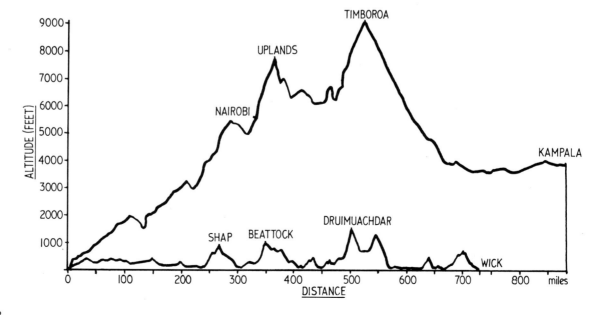

decided to standardise them, thus providing motive power capable of traversing the whole line, with obvious convenience and economy in operation.

Hence, in 1928—9 a further twenty Garratts were placed in service, essentially the same as their predecessors, but taking advantage of a slight relaxation in axle loading restrictions to increase the water tank capacity, while to suit the then current policy of the railway, they were arranged to burn coal, although eventually all were oil-fired. These locomotives, classed EC1 (EAR 50), were numbered 45—64 and apart from the two already mentioned which went to Indo-China, all survived to be taken over by the East African Railways as did all subsequent KUR Garratts. A further pair of EC1 class were built in 1930, and fitted with ACFI feed-water heaters above the boilers, giving them a rather French Colonial appearance. These, Nos 65 and 66, were given a different classification, 51, when taken over by the EAR. Scrapping of the EC1 class commenced in 1954, and all are now gone.

We now come to something of a mystery, the ten EC2 class Garratts (EAR 52), built by North British in 1931, EAR numbers 67—76. These were a slight variation of the EC1 class, having the same water capacity but rearranged so that an extra 100 gallons were carried in the front tank. Under what circumstances North British obtained the order is unknown but it would appear that they violated Beyer Peacock's patents, for they were never advertised by NBL as might otherwise have been the case. A pamphlet in the EAR drawing office at Nairobi, unfortunately not in the writer's possession, was issued by NBL describing the locomotives as 'North British Articulated Locomotives' although they were Garratts pure and simple. Whatever the details, Beyer Peacock's lawyers seem to have subsequently kept North British out of the Garratt market and the firm, in their final elaborate Beyer Garratt catalogue, avoided mention of the missing class by referring to the EC and EC1 classes as EC1 and EC2 respectively! Thus were all but those who knew the EAR prevented from learning the existence of these cuckoo-like interlopers. In fact, these NBL EC2s lasted much longer than their slightly earlier Beyer Peacock equivalents, and in October 1967 they were taken out of line service, from Tabora in Tanzania to where they had migrated.

*The Tanganyika version, class 53, mechanically the
same as classes 50 to 52. No 5302* Iringa *at Nairobi.*
EAR

The last three EC2s were transferred from
Tabora to Dar-es-Salaam in the late 1960s, where
they finished their lives on shunting and transfer
work. No 5210 has been preserved.

Having pioneered the 4—8—2 + 2—8—4 type in
1926, the KUR in 1939 became the first to use
another type, the 4—8—4 + 4—8—4 Class EC3
(EAR 57), an arrangement which included the
maximum number of wheels used under a
Garratt. These, when built, were the largest ever
used on 50lb rail and in addition to the extra two
pairs of wheels, a substantial increase in axle load
was permitted, this no doubt reflecting an
improvement in the road bed. Built right up to
the limit of the loading gauge then in existence,
these handsome machines were a remarkable
piece of engineering, and immediately trans-
formed the operating potential of the railway, not
only by their increased tractive effort and boiler
power, but also by their wheel diameter of 4ft 6in,
a substantial increase over the 3ft 7in of previous
Garratts and larger even than the 4ft 3in of the
heavy 2—8—2s.

The twelve engines were built in two batches in
1939 and 1940, being placed in service in 1939

and 1940—41 respectively, just in time to provide
a much-needed increase in motive power necessitated by the war. Numbered 77 to 88, they were
given attractive names of local origin, a practice
that was then extended to the other Garratts
and to the 2—8—2s.

For the first time in East Africa, bar frames
were built under a Garratt, a fact which contributed to their being able to stand up to thirty
years of really hard slogging work. Although
built in the hey-day of poppet valves, ordinary
piston valves of ample size were provided in the
straight-ported cylinders, a standard from which
East Africa never deviated. Compared with the
earlier locomotives, the drive was extended from
the second to the third coupled axle, as was Beyer
Peacock's latest practice, while the cylinders
were brought down to the horizontal, instead of
being fairly steeply inclined.

The Laird crossheads were underslung from
twin slidebars, an arrangement which has always
given satisfaction in East Africa. The valve gear,
as later became standard, was arranged so that
the radius rods were all at the bottom of the links
when running chimney first, and vice-versa. As in

180

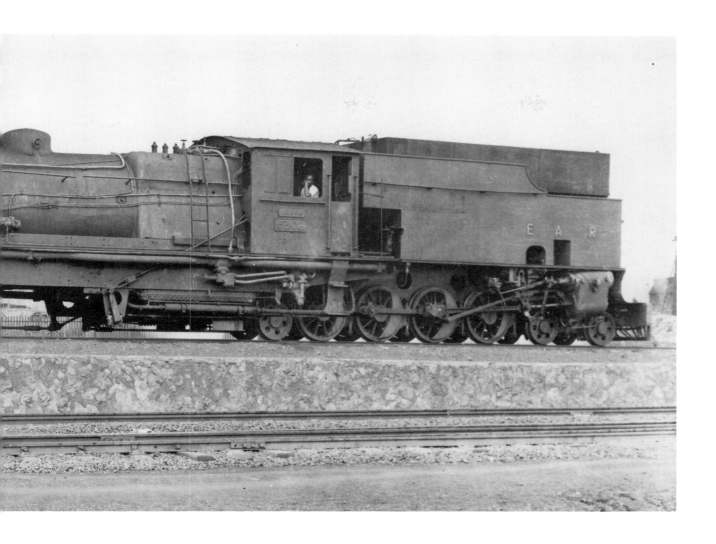

all subsequent Garratts built specifically for East Africa, the EC3s were built to be easily converted to 3ft 6in gauge anticipating an eventual link-up with the railways in Southern Africa. When the EC3s were built this seemed, and was, remote, but the main Kenya-Uganda and Tanzania systems have now been linked for some years, and the remarkable scheme for building the 1160-mile Tan-Zam railway, completed by the Chinese in 1976, and diesel worked, has brought a 3ft 6in link from Zambia right into metre gauge territory at Dar-es-Salaam. It remains to be seen whether it will be thought worth unifying the gauge in East Africa by conversion to Cape gauge. The difference between gauges is too small to allow for three-rail mixed gauge working.

The method used to ensure easy permanent gauge changing for existing metre gauge stock is simple and effective, and consists of manufacturing the wheel centres with wide rims, having a stepped profile, upon which the tyres are shrunk with rather more than one inch of the centre protruding outside. To convert to 3ft 6in-gauge, it is necessary only to remove the tyres and substitute new ones whose inner step will then position them

suitably for 3ft 6in gauge. The only other alteration necessary is to the brake gear which also can easily be re-gauged to suit the wheels. As the 3ft 6in-gauge lines of Southern Africa also have MCB couplers at 2ft 11in from rail level compared to the EAR 'chopper' couplers at 1ft 9in, these Garratts together, of course, with conventional locomotives and rolling stock, had been designed so that after removal of the old couplers, a simple alteration to the buffer beams would enable MCB couplers to be fitted. The only other difference is in brake system, Kenya and Uganda having air while the remaining countries use vacuum brakes. Here, if gauge conversion ever takes place, one hopes expediency will not compel East Africa to take the backward step of converting from air to vacuum, as indications are that the present 3ft 6in-gauge systems are thinking seriously of adopting air brakes themselves. Of course bogie and wheelset changing on passenger and freight stock (as practised between France and Spain) instead of a permanent track gauge alteration is another possibility.

To enable the EC3s to traverse curves of 275ft radius, the leading wheels of each unit were

The KUR class EC3, the world's first double 4—8—4 Garratt, and extremely handsome as first built to the restricted Indian loading gauge. No 80 Narok. Beyer Peacock

flangeless. Roller bearings were used, SKF spherical on the return cranks and Timken on the bogie axle-boxes, and these assisted in obtaining the high mileage run.

The round-top firebox contained two thermic syphons and was originally arranged to burn coal, although oil later became the fuel.

The performance of these locomotives was outstanding; not only could they haul 575 tons up uncompensated 1 in 50 gradients, but during their early years they soon established a reputation for high reliability and availability, running up to 6775 miles per month and 200,000 miles between general repairs, no mean figure for a single-track railway running over the fearsome gradients of the KUR.

Later, when the height of the loading gauge was raised from 12ft 6in to 13ft 6in, the EC3s had their chimneys and domes raised to suit, which rather detracted from their appearance. Under the

EAR they were one of the classes selected to be fitted with Giesl ejectors — and in this form they ended their lives working from Nairobi and Nakuru sheds, No 5711 being retained for preservation in Nairobi railway museum. Thus they were never converted to 3ft 6in gauge.

We now come to the wartime locomotives, of which a fuller description is given in Chapter 11. The KUR had two types of these, seven of the heavy type being especially built to metre gauge and as 4—8—2 + 2—8—4, these becoming Class EC4 (EAR 54) Nos 89 to 95, later Nos 100 to 106, and originally WD Nos 4418—24. The EC4s were by far the most powerful of the EAR Garratts from their introduction until the arrival of the 59

(right) Equipped with taller chimneys and domes, the EC3s, as EAR class 57, lost some of their impressiveness. 5701 Mengo at EAR's favourite photographic location. All were later fitted with Giesl ejectors. EAR

class eleven years later. However, being plate-framed jobs they were less robust than the other modern EAR Garratts and this, combined with their high power and small wheels, made them heavy on maintenance. The class worked their whole life on the KUR section, being too heavy for Tanganyika. Two of the light type 4—8—2 + 2—8—4s were also supplied, WD Nos 74242—3, KUR Class EC5 (EAR 55) Nos 120 and 121. To suit the main line, these EC5s had their coal and water capacities increased, but as will be seen later, the class had a reputation for wandering, and with others obtained from various sources, a few remained in service to the end of steam. Although plate-framed also, the EC5s were much less powerful than the EC4s, with larger wheels, and have not tended to tear themselves to pieces like the larger engines. This brings to an end the Garratts of the KUR, which were, however, perpetuated on the EAR as we shall later see.

The Tanganyika Railways

In its early days, under German rule, the TR, or rather its two constituents, comprised a typical German 'lokalbahn', transplanted to the wilds of Africa, and the locomotives, dinky eight-coupled and Mallet tanks, would have looked quite at home in the Thuringian forest. At a later stage they graduated to 2—8—0 tender engines, which had a very short life, and after Tanganyika became a British Protectorate the motive power went suddenly British, with the same types as on the KUR, some even being from that system.

Garratts were not introduced until 1931, when three were purchased, generally to the KUR EC1 design but with higher, narrower front tanks. These were used on the Dar-es-Salaam to Morogoro section, the heaviest part of the main line, it being general policy on the TR, with its lighter traffic, to use tender engines as standard and Garratts only for the heaviest duties. These three engines, Class GA Nos 300—302, later 700—702 and EAR 53, remained in service until the 1950s, when they were replaced by the later EAR 60 class, when the GAs were transferred to the KUR section. Latterly, however, they returned to home ground, and finally worked out their days on transfer work at Dar-es-Salaam, there being only two survivors, No 702 having been scrapped as a result of an accident before being taken over by the EAR.

The only other Tanganyika Garratts were four of the light WD type, TR Nos 750—53, which were acquired ex Burma Railways in 1948, and which the TR classified GB. These, like the KUR examples, became EAR Class 55.

East African Railways

The EAR, formed in 1948 by the amalgamation of the KUR and TR, inherited Garratts from both constituents, although mostly from the KUR. One of the first things which was done was to renumber and reclassify the locomotive stock, and in so doing a continental system was used whereby the engine class formed the first two figures of the engine number, a logical and sensible method which found no favour anywhere else in the British Empire other than New South Wales, and, today, with British Rail diesel and electric locomotives. Tank engines were Class 10 upwards, engine numbers 1001 etc, tender engines Class 20 upwards, and Garratts Classes 50 et seq. The KUR Classes EC1, EC1 (last two locomotives), EC2, EC3, EC4 and EC5 became respectively EAR Classes 50, 51, 52, 57, 54, and 55, while the TR Classes GA and GB became 53 and 55, the latter being the only type common to the two systems, although the 53s had most details common to the 50, 51, and 52 classes.

A number of locomotives was soon acquired, including six of a new class, 56, which were based upon the wartime 55 class, but differed in having 'streamlined' tanks and bunkers, and Belpaire fireboxes with arch tubes. In all major dimensions, and of course in haulage power and route availability, they were the equivalent of the war engines and even retained plate frames. These engines were placed in service shortly before the renumbering scheme, and thus carried for a short while Class EC6 and numbers 122 to 127, which were of course a continuation of the KUR system, although 'EAR' was carried on the tanks. Originally coal fired, they were later converted to burn oil, and while originally allocated to the KUR, were to be found at Dar-es-Salaam in Tanzania, before withdrawal.

Another class developed from an existing type was a further batch of EC3s, but with an extra ½in added to the cylinder diameter in the good old tradition of British locomotive engineering. Two rather continental features adopted, on this class only, were stovepipe chimneys and piston tail-rods. This class was built for oil burning and remained so. Original numbers were 89—106, soon changed to the 58 series, and they bore the initials EAR & H, standing for East African Railways and Harbours, although later classes reverted to EAR. The 58 class have always worked on the KUR system, putting up the same performance as the 57s, and were finally working around Nakuru.

It was on the 58s that the first significant tests, outside Europe, with the Giesl ejector were made, and the author is pleased that he played a modest part in the introduction of this device to East Africa, fuller details of which will follow later.

Developed from the 57 class were the 58s, built from the outset to the taller loading gauge. No 5813 is seen at Limuru in 1956, hauling a Nairobi-Nakuru passenger train. A. E. Durrant

In 1951 a further five 55 class were purchased from Burma, bringing their numbers to eleven. This class seemed the favourite 'stop-gap' type for providing additional power at various places when required, and in connection with this they have had their fuel and water capacities altered from time to time to suit the length of run or weight of track worked upon, and have also varied from coal to oil firing as required. For example, the two KUR locomotives had their coal and water supplies considerably increased, to run as main-line engines while at the other end of the scale, some, by then oil burning, had substantially reduced supplies to run on 40lb track. Thus the weights varied by as much as 12½ tons from the heaviest to the lightest of the same class.

In the mid-1950s all but 5507–9 were allocated to the Central line (Tanganyika), had vacuum brakes and burned coal, the odd three being air-braked oil-burners allocated to the KUR system. Thus, ironically, the two original KUR locomotives were on the Tanganyika system. By 1966, they had all moved around again, Nos 5501/3/11 being at Tororo in Uganda, 5505 at Moshi in Tanzania, and the remainder at Voi, in Kenya home of the last two survivors, used mainly on odd ballast workings, although one was noted on the Nairobi-Athi River pickup as late as 1975.

The next type to appear was the 60 class, which was yet another development of the 55 and 56 classes, being identical in most respects with the latter except that more water and less fuel are

185

carried, while the boiler mountings are built up higher to take advantage of the new loading gauge. In fact, the original batch of 60s were originally ordered as Nos 5607—18, but at the time of delivery, in 1954, it was decided to classify them separately, and the 59 class being already on order, they perforce became Class 60. Twenty-nine were built, all in 1954, and while Beyer Peacock won the order, the first twelve were sub-let to Franco-Belge. Originally, only 6009—10 were allocated to Tanganyika, the others being on the KUR, but nine were later in Tanzania and had been allocated to Dar-es-Salaam. By November 1967 they were being replaced there by diesels and moved up-country to Tabora. The remainder were scattered between Kampala and Tororo in Uganda, Nairobi and Nakuru in Kenya, and Moshi in Tanzania. The 60s were the first EAR class to receive the new magnificent maroon livery which became standard, and in which other classes were later painted as they passed through shops. This colour originally belonged to the Tanganyika Railway, and was transplanted to the EAR with the new CME, W. Bulman, in the 1950s. Officially, all the 60 class are withdrawn, but some were noted in 1979—80 deputising for failed diesels on the branch from Voi. Some were also left in Uganda during the reign of Idi Amin, where, being inedible, they probably remain, although it is doubtful whether they ever steam.

We now come to the final EAR class, the magnificent 59s, which are the largest and most powerful locomotives ever built for the metre gauge. Not only this, they are the largest locomotives built for Africa and, with the demise of the American steam giants, the largest steam locomotives in regular service in the world during the 1970s. In the early 1950s traffic on the Mombasa-Nairobi section of the main Kenya-Uganda line was approaching its maximum with existing power and, in fact, it soon became a bottleneck, with exports and imports to and from Mombasa being seriously delayed by the inadequate transport inland. Doubling the track was out of the question, both in time and expense, as was also electrification, which was seriously considered.

Fortunately, it was clear that the track could support far larger power than was available at the time. The 54 class Garratts, the most powerful on the system, had a 14 ton axle load and 58,000lb tractive effort, while there were also the 28 class 2—8—2s with a 17½ ton axle load and 38,000lb tractive effort. Allowing for diminution of water supplies, a Garratt with the 2—8—2's axle load could be built with 70,000lb tractive effort. This increase, while substantial, was not thought sufficient, and careful investigations into track stresses, by modern analytical, although

empirical, methods showed that given a 'tapered' axle loading, a maximum of 21 tons, and an average of 20 tons per axle was feasible. Armed with this, CME 'Willie' Bulman went ahead and laid down the specification of these mightiest of African Garratts, eclipsed only by the solitary Я.01 built for Russia. Even so, the EAR locomotive had a greater axle load and adhesion weight than the Soviet engine, and within the restricted loading gauge of the EAR the 59 class design must have presented numerous problems for Beyer Peacock's drawing office at Gorton.

Apart from its size, the 59 possessed no technical peculiarities, being a large hunk of sound engineering, and the EAR were so confident of Beyer Peacock's competence to design a sound job, that before delivery of the first locomotive, the original order for nine, placed in 1950, had grown to thirty-four. This five-year gap, from order to delivery, was typical of the locomotive market at the time, with swollen order books for much-needed power necessary to cope with the post-war boom in traffic. As we have seen with the 60 class, and indeed elsewhere, Beyer Peacocks were so swamped with work that they were sub-letting substantial orders for Garratts to other firms, home and overseas, in the mid-fifties. Yet a decade later, they had built not only their last steam but their last diesel, and the drawing office which designed the mighty 59s lay silent, each board under its dust-sheet. In the works which Charles Beyer and Richard Peacock had built up over a century beforehand, shops were closed down, and all the substantial paraphernalia of locomotive building, the patterns, jigs, flanging blocks, and the like, were lying around as scrap.

However, to return to the more cheerful subject of the 59 class, these were, as might be expected, built on bar frames, 4½in thick, the distance between frames being only two feet. For the first time in East Africa, all axles, both driving and bogie, had roller bearings, supplied by Timken. The big ends also had rollers, these being supplied by Skefco, although they were later replaced by Timken bearings, which were thus now used throughout the locomotive.

Straightforward large diameter straight-ported piston valves admit steam to the cylinders, and the Hadfield power reverse is fitted. The wheels are 4ft 6in diameter, as on the 57 and 58 classes, but unlike these earlier locomotives, all tyres are flanged, although the two intermediate pairs on each unit have thin flanges.

The boiler is of immense size, 7ft 6in diameter, or well over twice the rail gauge. The fireboxes were round topped, radially stayed, and from the beginning the locomotives were arranged to burn oil, although provision was made for fitting a mechanical stoker should conditions dictate a

(above) Bowling along the Moshi-Voi link, with negligible load, No 6023 has gained a Giesl ejector but lost its colonial 'Governor' name since delivery from Beyer Peacock.   A. E. Durrant

(below) No 5921 Mount Nyiru rolls a long freight through a typically well kept wayside station, twenty years of Kenya's hardest work resting lightly on its mighty frames. Two large diesels were, of course, needed to replace each 59 class in haulage capacity. A. E. Durrant

return to coal firing. Despite their power, a straightforward single chimney was fitted, although Goodfellow tips were included in the blastpipe. Tanks were, of course, of the 'stream-lined' form, and the sides of the front tank were angled inboard to give better visibility. It might be mentioned here that the EAR policy is to run their Garratts chimney first, turning at each end of the run generally being by means of triangles, although a 100ft turntable is installed at Nairobi.

The designed performance of the 59s was to haul 1200 tons over 1 in 66 gradients on normal schedules and this was substantially exceeded on test, although the couplers used by the EAR are barely up to taking this load, and there have been cases of the 59s straightening out the coupler hook instead of pulling the train. Incidentally, to give some idea of the possible performance of a 59, before delivery, test runs were made with a pair of 54s. The 59s did their job splendidly, and within a year of their arrival the back-log at Mombasa had cleared, and traffic was functioning normally. This, perhaps, is a pity, for Bulman was already thinking in terms of a 61 class which, as it turned out, was never required. This colossus would have eclipsed all other Garratts built, and brought to East Africa's metre gauge rails something bigger than the majority of USA Class 1 railroads ever possessed! With a 26 ton axle load, which the 95lb track to Nairobi had been estimated to support, a tractive effort of 110,000lb was feasible, and to feed this a boiler 8ft 3in diameter was proposed. A 4—8—4 + 4—8—4 arrangement was envisaged, with 4ft 9in wheels, and the whole ensemble, gargantuan though it was, still looked rather like a 59 and by no means unwieldy. However, the 61 was not to be, and further developments in EAR Garratts consisted in upgrading their performance by means of the Giesl ejector.

It was in late 1955 that the author moved from Swindon to the EAR drawing office in Nairobi, having been previously in correspondence with Dr Giesl-Gieslingen in Vienna, who sent full details out for submission to the CME. Willie Bulman at once grasped the significance of the device and following the usual preliminaries, the first trial Giesl ejector was fitted to No 6029 in 1957. Success led to further trials, on 58, 59 and 60 classes in 1959, and commencing in 1961, a full-scale 'Gieslisation' programme was instituted, covering all post-war locomotives other than the 13 class 4—8—2T/4—8—4T.

While fuel economies were effected, the principal use of the Giesl ejector on the EAR was to increase available power and, of course, under EAR conditions with long periods of hard steaming, the potential reduction in back pressure was immense, and realised. The excellent results obtained were such that for the 58 class, the first class to be completely equipped, the working timetable for 1962 showed, for example, separate timings for 'goods' and 'Giesl goods'. From Kampala to Eldoret the respective booked timings were 961 and 778 minutes, a saving of three hours attributable to the better uphill performance of the Giesl equipped loco-motives. Similarly, a reduction in the stopping time for locomotive purposes was possible, due to fuel and water economy, and from Eldoret to Kampala, for example, eight stops totalling 55—63 minutes were allowed for the 'Mail', with only four stops amounting to 34 minutes for the 'Giesl Mail'. Under the circumstances, it was not surprising that other classes, including conven-tional locomotives, were fitted, and the pro-gramme, for Garratts, was as below:

EAR-GIESL GARRATTS

Year	Garratt class	Quantity
1957	60	1
1959	58	1
,,	59	1
,,	60	1
1960	58	17
1962	57	12
1964	55	11
,,	56	6
,,	59	1
,,	60	26
1967/7	59	32

A complete list of EAR Garratts, engine by engine, is appended below, together with a further table showing their principal dimensions.

The once proud East African Railways are no more, the confederation having broken up into the member states of Kenya, Tanzania (formerly Tanganyika) and Uganda, each with their own portion of the railway. In Kenya, the 59 and 60 classes of Garratt just survived into 1980, and 5918 has been preserved. Hopefully, the railway authorities may see fit to retain some steam in working order for tourist trains, to recreate for posterity the magnificent sight of a maroon Garratt climbing the Mau escarpments with a train of chocolate and cream carriages.

KUR No	EAR No	Builder	Works No	Date	Name	KUR Class	Remarks
41	—	BP	6300	/26		EC ⎞	Sold to Indo-China 1939,
42	—	,,	6301	/26		,, ⎟	numbered 201-204. Shipped
43	—	,,	6302	/26		,, ⎬	MS *Scheer*, ex Mombasa
44	—	,,	6303	/26		,, ⎠	4/8/39
45	5001	,,	6429	/28		EC1	
46	5002	,,	5430	/ ,,		,,	
47	5003	,,	6431	/ ,,	*Toro*	,,	
48	5004	,,	6432	/ ,,	*Masai*	,,	
49	5005	,,	6433	/ ,,	*Nyanzi*	,,	
50	5006	,,	6434	/ ,,	*Meru*	,,	
51	—	,,	6435	/ ,,		,,	Indo-China No 205
52	5007	,,	6436	/ ,,	*Masaka*	,,	
53	—	,,	6437	/ ,,		,,	Indo-China No 206
54	5008	,,	6438	/ ,,	*Nandi*	,,	
55	5009	,,	6439	/ ,,	*Bunyoro*	,,	
56	5010	,,	6440	/ ,,		,,	
57	5011	,,	6516	/ ,,	*Kikuyu*	,,	Tanga Line 6/53
58	5012	,,	6517	/ ,,	*Ankole*	,,	,, ,, ,,
59	5013	,,	6518	/ ,,		,,	
60	5014	,,	6519	/ ,,		,,	
61	5015	,,	6520	/ ,,		,,	
62	5016	,,	6521	/ ,,	*Londiani*	,,	
63	5017	,,	6522	/ ,,	*Ukamba*	,,	
64	5018	,,	6523	/ ,,	*Machakos*	,,	
65	5101	,,	6637	/30	*Laikipia*	,,	
66	5102	,,	6638	/ ,,		,,	
67	5201	NBL	24070	/31	*Busoga*	EC2	
68	5202	,,	24071	/ ,,	*Kavirondo*	,,	
69	5203	,,	24072	/ ,,	*Mubendi*	,,	
70	5204	,,	24073	/ ,,	*Turkana*	,,	
71	5205	,,	24074	/ ,,	*Nyeri*	,,	
72	5206	,,	24075	/ ,,	*Kiambu*	,,	
73	5207	,,	24076	/ ,,	*Nzoia*	,,	
74	5208	,,	24077	/ ,,	*Isolo*	,,	
75	5209	,,	24078	/ ,,	*Nakuru*	,,	
76	5210	,,	24079	/ ,,	*Entebbe*	,,	Preserved
700*	5301	BP	6718	/ ,,	*Arusha*	GA*	
701*	5302	,,	6719	/ ,,	*Iringa*	,,	
702*	—	,,	6720	/ ,,	*Bukoba*	,,	
89	5401	,,	7075	/44		EC4	Ex WD 4418, 2nd KUR No 100
90	5402	,,	7076	/ ,,		,,	Ex WD 4419, 101
91	5403	,,	7077	/ ,,		,,	Ex WD 4420, 102
92	5404	,,	7078	/ ,,		,,	Ex WD 4421, 103
93	5405	,,	7079	/ ,,		,,	Ex WD 4422, 104
94	5406	,,	7080	/ ,,		,,	Ex WD 4423, 105
95	5407	,,	7081	/ ,,		,,	Ex WD 4424, 106
120	5501	,,	7158	/45		EC5	Ex WD 74242
121	5502	,,	7159	/ ,,		,,	Ex WD 74243
750*	5503	,,	7150	/ ,,		GB*	Ex WD 74234 ⎞ Ex Burma Rlys
751*	5504	,,	7151	/ ,,		,,	Ex WD 74235 ⎟ Nos 851-854
752*	5505	,,	7157	/ ,,		,,	Ex WD 74241 ⎬ in 1948
753*	5506	,,	7146	/ ,,		,,	Ex WD 74230 ⎠
—	5507	,,	7155	/45		— ⎞	Ex Burma Rly Class GD/1951
—	5508	,,	7154	/ ,,		— ⎟	5507-09 temporarily 5527-29
—	5509	,,	7149	/ ,,		— ⎬	3400G water, 1200G oil with
—	5510	,,		/ ,,		— ⎟	reduced water capacity for
—	5511	,,		/ ,,		— ⎠	Tanga Line (40lb track).
122	5601	,,	7280	/49		EC6	Burma Railways Nos 865-9.
123	5602	,,	7281	/ ,,		,,	Built for Burma, Class 'GE'
124	5603	,,	7282	/ ,,		,,	
125	5604	,,	7283	/ ,,		,,	
126	5605	,,	7284	/ ,,		,,	
127	5606	,,	7285	/ ,,		,,	
77	5701	,,	6905	/39	*Mengo*	EC3	
78	5702	,,	6906	/ ,,	*Teso*	,,	
79	5703	,,	6907	/ ,,	*Usaingishu*	,,	
80	5704	,,	6908	/ ,,	*Narok*	,,	
81	5705	,,	6909	/ ,,	*Marakwet*	,,	
82	5706	,,	6910	/ ,,	*Wajir*	,,	
83	5707	,,	6970	/40	*Chua*	EC3	
84	5708	,,	6971	/ ,,	*Gulu*	,,	
85	5709	,,	6972	/ ,,	*Lango*	,,	
86	5710	,,	6973	/ ,,	*Budama*	,,	
87	5711	,,	6974	/ ,,	*Karamoja*	,,	Preserved
88	5712	,,	6975	/ ,,	*Kigenzi*	,,	
89	5801	,,	7290	/49		,,	
90	5802	,,	7291	/ ,,		,,	
91	5803	,,	7292	/ ,,		,,	
92	5804	,,	7293	/ ,,		,,	
93	5805	,,	7294	/ ,,		,,	
94	5806	,,	7295	/ ,,		,,	
95	5807	,,	7296	/ ,,		,,	

KUR No	EAR No	Builder	Works No	Date	Name	KUR Class	Remarks
96	5808	,,	7297	/ ,,		,,	
97	5809	,,	7298	/ ,,		,,	
98	5810	,,	7299	/ ,,		,,	
99	5811	,,	7300	/ ,,		,,	
100	5812	,,	7301	/ ,,		,,	
101	5813	,,	7302	/ ,,		,,	
102	5814	,,	7303	/ ,,		,,	
103	5815	,,	7304	/ ,,		,,	
104	5816	,,	7305	/ ,,		,,	
105	5817	,,	7306	/ ,,		,,	
106	5818	,,	7307	/ ,,		,,	
—	5901	,,	7632	/55	*Mount Kenya*	—	
—	5902	,,	7633	/ ,,	*Ruwenzori Mountains*	—	
—	5903	,,	7634	/ ,,	*Mount Meru*	—	
—	5904	,,	7635	/ ,,	*Mount Elgon*	—	
—	5905	,,	7636	/ ,,	*Mount Muhavura*	—	
—	5906	,,	7637	/ ,,	*Mount Sattima*	—	
—	5907	,,	7638	/ ,,	*Mount Kinangop*	—	
—	5908	,,	7639	/ ,,	*Mount Loolmalasin*	—	
—	5909	,,	7640	/ ,,	*Mount Mgahinga*	—	
—	5910	,,	7641	/ ,,	*Mount Hanang*	—	
—	5911	,,	7642	/ ,,	*Mount Sekerri*	—	
—	5912	,,	7643	/ ,,	*Mount Oldeani*	—	
—	5913	,,	7644	/ ,,	*Mount Debasien*	—	
—	5914	,,	7645	/ ,,	*Mount Londiani*	—	
—	5915	,,	7646	/ ,,	*Mount Mtorwi*	—	
—	5916	,,	7647	/ ,,	*Mount Rungwe*	—	
—	5917	,,	7648	/ ,,	*Mount Kitumbeine*	—	
—	5918	,,	7649	/ ,,	*Mount Gelai*	—	Preserved
—	5919	,,	7650	/ ,,	*Mount Lengai*	—	
—	5920	,,	7651	/ ,,	*Mount Mbeya*	—	
—	5921	,,	7652	/ ,,	*Mount Nyiru*	—	
—	5922	,,	7653	/ ,,	*Mount Blackett*	—	
—	5923	,,	7654	/ ,,	*Mount Longonot*	—	
—	5924	,,	7655	/ ,,	*Mount Eburu*	—	
—	5925	,,	7656	/ ,,	*Mount Monduli*	—	
—	5926	,,	7657	/ ,,	*Mount Kimhandu*	—	
—	5927	,,	7658	/ ,,	*Mount Tinderet*	—	
—	5928	,,	7700	/ ,,	*Mount Kilimanjaro*	—	
—	5929	,,	7701	/ ,,	*Mount Longido*	—	
—	5930	,,	7702	/ ,,	*Mount Shengena*	—	
—	5931	,,	7703	/ ,,	*Uluguru Mountains*	—	
—	5932	,,	7704	/ ,,	*Ol'Donya Sabuk*	—	
—	5933	,,	7705	/ ,,	*Mount Suswa*	—	
—	5934	,,	7706	/ ,,	*Menengai Crater*	—	
—	6001	FR B	2983	/54	*Sir Geoffrey Archer*	—	⎫
—	6002	,,	2984	/ ,,	*Sir Hesketh Bell*	—	
—	6003	,,	2985	/ ,,	*Sir Stewart Symes*	—	
—	6004	,,	2986	/ ,,	*Sir Frederick Jackson*	—	
—	6005	,,	2987	/ ,,	*Sir Bernard Bourdillon*	—	
—	6006	,,	2988	/ ,,	*Sir Harold MacMichael*	—	Ordered as EAR 5607-18
—	6007	,,	2989	/ ,,	*Sir Mark Young*	—	BP Nos 7565-76 allocated
—	6008	,,	2990	/ ,,	*Sir Wilfred Jackson*	—	Names later removed
—	6009	,,	2991	/ ,,	*Sir Edward Twining*	—	
—	6010	,,	2992	/ ,,	*Sir Donald Cameron*	—	
—	6011	,,	2993	/ ,,	*Sir William Battershill*	—	
—	6012	,,	2994	/ ,,	*Sir Percy Girouard*	—	
—	6013	,,	7577	/ ,,	*Sir Henry Belfield*	—	⎭
—	6014	,,	7578	/ ,,	*Sir Joseph Byrne*	—	⎫
—	6015	,,	7579	/ ,,	*Sir Robert Brooke-Popham*	—	
—	6016	,,	7580	/ ,,	*Sir Henry Moore*	—	
—	6017	,,	7659	/ ,,	*Sir John Hall*	—	
—	6018	,,	7660	/ ,,	*Sir Charles Dundas*	—	
—	6019	,,	7661	/ ,,	*Sir Philip Mitchel*	—	
—	6020	,,	7662	/ ,,	*Sir Evelyn Baring*	—	Names later removed
—	6021	,,	7663	/ ,,	*Sir William Gowers*	—	
—	6022	,,	7664	/ ,,	*Sir Andrew Cohen*	—	
—	6023	,,	7665	/ ,,	*Sir Edward Northey*	—	
—	6024	,,	7666	/ ,,	*Sir James Hayes-Sadler*	—	
—	6025	,,	7721	/ ,,	*Sir Henry Colville*	—	⎭
—	6026	,,	7722	/ ,,	*Sir Horace Byatt*	—	Renamed *Uhuru*
—	*6027*	,,	*7723*	/ ,,	*Sir Gerald Portal*	—	⎫
—	6028	,,	7724	/ ,,	*Sir H. H. Johnston*	—	Names later removed
—	6029	,,	7725	/ ,,	*Sir Edward Grigg*	—	⎭

*Tanganyika Rlys

EAST AFRICA

Class	Type	Cylinders Dia × Stroke (in)	Coupled Wheel Dia (ft in)	Boiler Press (psi)	Tractive Effort @ 85% (lb)	Grate Area (sq ft)	Max Boiler Dia (Outs) (ft in)	Heating Surface — Fire-box	Heating Surface — Tubes	Heating Surface — Super-heater	Weights — Max Axle	Weights — Ad-hesive	Weights — Total	Water Cpcty (Gal)	Fuel Cpcty (Tons/Gal)	Literature Reference	Remarks
EC	4-8-2 + 2-8-4	16½×22	3-7	170	40260	43·6	6-0	174	1863	380	10·0	79·35	125·35	4250	6t	W218	Coal Burning
50	4-8-2 + 2-8-4	16½×22	3-7	170	40260	43·6	6-0	174	1863	380	10·55	88·9	138·15	5250	2375g		Large Oil Tank }
											12·0	85·15	132·7	5250	1417g		Small Oil Tank }
50	4-8-2 + 2-8-4	16½×22	3-7	170	40260	43·6	6-0	174	1863	380	10·9	88·9	138·15	5250	5t		Coal Burning }
											12·0	82·35	131·95	5250	2375g		Oil Burning }
51	4-8-2 + 2-8-4	16½×22	3-7	170	40260	43·6	6-0	174	1863	380	10·9	87·95	142·1	4750	5t	L364/30	Coal Burning }
											11·6	80·0	131·35	5250	2375g		Oil Burning }
52	4-8-2 + 2-8-4	16½×22	3-7	170	40260	43·6	6-0	174	1863	380	10·9	83·75	138·3	4250	6t		Coal Burning }
																	Oil Burning }
53	4-8-2 + 2-8-4	16½×22	3-7	170	40260	43·6	6-0	194	1868	380				6000	2480g		
54	4-8-2 + 2-8-4	19×24	3-9½	180	51400	51·3	7-0	212	2328	470	14·0	112·0	171·5	4925	2375g		
55	4-8-2 + 2-8-4	16×24	4-0	200	38400	48·75	6-0	183	1813	399	20·35	81·55	139·0	4200	7t		KUR—as delivered
											11·25	86·6	146·3	5300	10t		KUR—altered for Main Line } Coal Burning
56	4-8-2 + 2-8-4	16×24	4-0	200	38400	48·75	6-0	163	1813	399	10·7	84·8	133·45	3400	1200g		Nos 5507-9, Modified 1954 } Oil Burning
											10·7	84·8	144·0	4500	1900g		Standard }
											11·0	88·0	146·75	4200	2375g		Oil Burning }
											11·0	88·0	146·75				
57	4-8-4 + 4-8-4	16×26	4-6	220	41650	48·5	6-6¼	190	1779	370	11·75	94·0	186·3	4200	11·5t	L272/39	Coal Burning }
58	4-8-4 + 4-8-4	16½×26	4-6	220	43300	48·5	6-6¼	234	1981	477	11·75	94·0	186·25	6000	12·0t	G94/39	Coal Burning }
								169	1981	477	11·75	94·0	186·25	6000	2375g	L90/55	Oil Burning }
59	4-8-2 + 2-8-4	20½×28	4-6	225	73500	72·0	7-6	247	3313	747	21·0	159·53	251·68	8600	2700g	L144/55	Coal Burning
60	4-8-2 + 2-8-4	16×24	4-0	200	38400	48·75	6-0	170	1755	370	11·0	86·86	152·3	4612	1800g	L170/55	Oil Burning

191

Chapter 11

War Locomotives

The engines covered in this chapter are grouped together for convenience, and while they are referred to in the chapters and paragraphs dealing with the railways upon which they operated, more detailed descriptions are given here, together with their rather complex disposals and travels.

There are two distinct groups of War Garratts, both built in the latter stages of the 1939–45 war, and both to assist mainly in the supply situation connected with the Pacific war.

Most war engines were simple two-cylinder rigid engines, rugged, and suitable for extended use under poor maintenance conditions, the 2–8–0, 2–8–2, and 2–10–0 types being those mainly constructed. For the narrow, that is metre and 3ft 6in-gauge lines, the USA 'MacArthur' 2–8–2 was the standard war engine, being built by the hundred for these lines. However, these were small engines, and greater power was needed on a number of lines, some of which could support a heavier axle load than these 2–8–2s.

It is a tribute to the basic simplicity of the Garratt concept that it was considered suitable for war-time conditions, over one hundred being built. The two groups consisted firstly of those built by Beyer Peacock, for the British War Department and, secondly, those built in Australia for the Commonwealth Land Transport Board.

Dealing first with the WD engines, the spreading of the war to the Far East, plus the necessity of obtaining additional raw material from Africa, led to the need for additional high-powered locomotives and, to ensure the maximum degree of standardisation, these were built for the WD. Nevertheless, five different classes, two heavy and three light, were built, this being a more or less inevitable outcome of the need for speed in construction, as we shall see.

The heavy type was built for Africa, basically to 3ft 6in-gauge, and was modelled on the SAR GE class 2–8–2 + 2–8–2, as the design nearest to that required, although the straight-ported cylinders and round-top boiler were more in line with the Rhodesian Railways 16th class.

(right) An interesting transition. WD heavy Garratt running as RR Mashonaland No 287, and fitted with German style chimney extension. This locomotive later went to Mozambique, and was fitted with a permanent chimney of taller proportions.
W. H. C. Kelland

Heavy steel slab being needed for such priority requirements as battleship armour, the design had perforce to be content with plate frames. The boilers were, of course, superheated and had arch tubes in the firebox, but were not fired mechanically.

Seventeen of this type were built, of which six went to the Gold Coast Railways, where they hauled 1100 ton trains of bauxite, until with-

drawn from service in 1960. Three were allocated to the Chemins de Fer Congo Ocean where they worked trains of up to 1000 tons, until this line was dieselised in 1959, whereupon they were sold to the Moçambique Railways. The remaining nine engines went to the Rhodesia Railways as their 18th class and were originally used in assisting the 16th class on the Wankie coal traffic. However they, too, were eventually sold to the CFM where, with their ex CO companions, they are still nominally at work.

For the Kenya Uganda Railway, of metre gauge, where a heavier axle load was permitted and more water capacity was required, the locomotive was redesigned as a 4—8—2 + 2—8—4 and seven were built for this line. All possible details of these engines were kept standard with the

3ft 6in-gauge 2—8—2 + 2—8—2, whilst the engines themselves were built to be easily convertible to that gauge.

The light type Garratts, designed with the Far East campaign in mind, were of three designs, with 2—8—0, 2—8—2, and 4—8—2 power units.

The first ten, 2—8—0 + 0—8—2, were a virtual duplicate of the Burma Railways GA^{III} class, the last at the time that Beyer Peacock had built for Burma, and the only eight-coupled, metre-gauge design with a ten-ton axle load available. As will be seen by reference to Chapter 4, the Burma Railways already had in mind the modification of the design to a 2—8—2 + 2—8—2, but for speed of delivery, ten were built to the original design while drawings for the modified type were being

The EAR 55 class came from diverse sources, burnt coal or oil, and were eventually Giesl-equipped. No 5505 at Nairobi in 1975 was a late survivor, and was about to haul the Athi River pickup freight. A. E. Durrant

prepared, whereupon fourteen of these were supplied.

Nevertheless, something larger again was really required, and the third metre-gauge design has an interesting history, spanning as it does four continents.

Just before the Second World War, the Great Western Railway of Brazil placed with Beyer Peacock an order for four metre-gauge 4—8—2 + 2—8—4 Garratts which had not been completed because of the war but for which, nevertheless, much design work had been done. These were exactly the sort of thing that the WD were

looking for and so, naturally, the drawings were taken out, dusted, and such modifications as necessary made to fit the engines into India's restricted loading gauge. Twenty were ordered and apart from their increased dimensions they were the counterpart of the Burma designs, being superheated jobs with round-top fireboxes, and with plate-framed power units. They were considered the light standard 4—8—2 + 2—8—4 but of course had little in common with the heavy type, having been evolved from an entirely different source.

This light 4—8—2 + 2—8—4 represents a

particularly successful attempt on Beyer Peacock's part as, following the wartime engines which worked in India, Burma, and East Africa, the design was also supplied to the South Australian Railways, some of these being built under licence by Franco-Belge. The original Brazilian order, plus another two locomotives, was eventually supplied under licence by Henschel, to the modernised post-war design virtually identical to the EAR 60 and South Australian 400 classes, and delivered to the North Eastern Railway of Brazil.

Building details are as tabulated right:

The distribution of these locomotives, together with their subsequent wanderings, is shown in the table overleaf.

WD Nos	Type	Gauge	Beyer Peacock Nos	Date
74200-09	2-8-0 + 0-8-2	Metre	7112-21	1943
74210-23	2-8-2 + 2-8-2	Metre	7122-35	1944
74224-25	4-8-2 + 2-8-4	Metre	7140-41	1944
74226-43	4-8-2 + 2-8-4	Metre	7142-59	1945
74400-17*	2-8-2 + 2-8-2	3ft 6in	7057-74	1943
74418-24*	4-8-2 + 2-8-4	Metre	7075-81	1943

*Heavy type

					(1945)							
74200	BAR	702	WD (India)	410	Burma Rlys	821						
74201	,,	703	,,	411	,,	822						
74202	,,	704	,,	412	,,	823						
74203	,,	701	,,	413	,,	824						
74204	,,	705	,,	414	,,	825						
74205	,,	706	,,	415	,,	826						
74206	,,	707	,,	416	,,	829						
74207	,,	708	,,	417	,,	830						
74208	,,	709	,,	418	,,	827						
74209	,,	710	,,	419	,,	828						
74210	Lost at sea											
74211	,,											
74212	WD (India)	420			Burma Rlys	841						
74213	,,	407			,,	838						
74214	BAR	711	WD (India)	400	,,	831						
74215	,,	712	,,	401	,,	832						
74216	WD (India)	402			,,	833						
74217	,,	403			,,	834						
74218	,,	404			,,	835						
74219	,,	405			,,	836						
74220	,,	421			,,	842						
74221	,,	409			,,	840						
74222	,,	406			,,	837						
74223	,,	408			,,	839						
74224	BAR	680	Assam Rly	680	NER/NEFR	975	ISR	32082				
74225	,,	681	,,	681	,,	976	,,	32083				
74226	,,	682	,,	682	,,	977	,,	32084				
74227	,,	683	,,	683	,,	978	,,	32085				
74228	,,	684	,,	684	,,	979	,,	32086				
74229	,,	685	,,	685	,,	980	,,	32087				
74230	,,	686	Burma Rlys	854	TR	753	EAR	5506				
74231	,,	687	,,	855	Burma Rlys	865	,,	5507				
74232	,,	688	,,	856	,,	866	,,	5508				
74233	,,	689	,,	857	,,	867	,,	5509				
74234	,,	690	WD (India)	422	,,	851	TR	750	EAR	5503		
74235	,,	691	,,	423	,,	852	,,	751	,,	5504		
74236	,,	692	Assam Rly	692	NER/NEFR	981	ISR	32088				
74237	,,	693	,,	693	,,	982	,,	32089				
74238	,,	694	Burma Rlys	858	Burma Rlys	868	EAR	5510				
74239	,,	695	,,	859	,,	869	,,	5511				
74240	,,	696	Assam Rly	696	NER/NEFR	983	ISR	32090				
74241	,,	697	Burma Rlys	853	TR	752	EAR	5505				
74242	KUR	120	EAR	5501								
74243	,,	121	,,	5502								
74400	GCR	301										
74401	,,	302										
74402	,,	303										
74403	,,	304										
74404	,,	305										
74405	,,	306										
74406	Congo		CFM	990								
74407	,,		,,	991								
74408	,,		,,	992								
74409	RR	281	,,	981								
74410	,,	282	,,	982								
74411	,,	283	,,	983								
74412	,,	284	,,	984								
74413	,,	285	,,	985								
74414	,,	286	,,	986								
74415	,,	287	,,	987								
74416	,,	288	,,	988								
74417	,,	289	,,	989								
74418	KUR	89	KUR	100	EAR	5401						
74419	,,	90	,,	101	,,	5402						
74420	,,	91	,,	102	,,	5403						
74421	,,	92	,,	103	,,	5404						
74422	,,	93	,,	104	,,	5405						
74423	,,	94	,,	105	,,	5406						
74424	,,	95	,,	106	,,	5407						

The Australian Standard Garratt

The ASG, as it was always known, was the result of a sudden strain being thrown on the railways of Queensland due to the Japanese-Allied war. The 1939 locomotive mileage of 16,081,602 had by 1942—3 increased to 24,309,794, an increase of 51 per cent, and it was felt that the introduction of Garratts would alleviate the problem.

Beyer Peacock being busy with the British WD Garratts, and the WAGR Midland Junction workshops having already built Garratts, the obvious step was taken of having the required engines built in Australia.

*The last survivor of the unfortunate Australian
Standard Garratt class awaits preservation at North
Williamstown, Victoria. It is expected that this
locomotive may run again within a reasonable future.*
A. E. Durrant

An existing Beyer Peacock design could have
been used, or could have been modified slightly to
suit, but the WAGR CME, Mr F. Mills, set to and
designed a new engine from scratch. These 4—8—2
+ 2—8—4 did not look right, and in fact were not
right.

The components were largely made by outside
works and assembled either in railway workshops
or at the Clyde Locomotive Works. Such were the
various faults detected in the design by the other
Australian CMEs that the Victorian Rly CME
refused to fit Newport works builder's plates to
those assembled there, refusing to be responsible
for such unsatisfactory locomotives.

After the war, the WAGR enginemen refused
to operate them, and a Royal Commission was
held, as a result of which thirty-six fairly major

alterations had to be made before the crews would
climb aboard.

These gave the engines of the WAGR at least a
life of about ten years, some being sold to other
railways, but the Queensland railways were so
disgusted that they ordered new Garratts from
Beyer Peacock, as did the South Australian
Railways, who ran them for little more than a
year.

Apparently the complete design had taken but
three months, a circumstance under which it was
hardly surprising that many features had not
been thought out properly, and over 100
scattered firms had contributed to the
construction.

The design comprised a 4—8—2 + 2—8—4 with
plate frames and piston-valve cylinders. The

197

leading and main driving wheels in each unit were flangeless whilst the tyres, after being shrunk on, were welded to the wheel centres. Boilers had Belpaire fireboxes, and an overall 'skyline' casing from smokebox to cab, a form of styling which one would hardly associate with an austerity war-time engine, while the same could be said for the streamlined front and rear tanks.

The boiler frame had large triangular holes slotted out for the purpose of reducing weight, the boiler itself being domeless, but with safety valves mounted on a manhole cover in the usual dome position.

It now remains to set out in tabular form the building and disposal of these 65 engines, some of which were never even assembled. The builders were:

CLTB Nos	Builder	Builders' Nos	Date
1-4	Newport	—	1943
5-10	,,	—	1944
11-20	Islington	—	1943-4
21-25	Clyde	467, 472-76	1944
26-30	Midland Jc	—	1943-4
31-33	Newport	—	1945
34-36	Not assembled	—	—
37-38	Clyde	492-93	1945
39-43	Not assembled	—	—
44-45	Islington	—	1945
46-50	Midland Jc	—	1945
51-53	Clyde	477-79	1944
54-65	,,	480-91	1945

The users of these engines are shown in the further table below:

CLTB No	First railway	Second railway
1- 5	QGR	—
6 & 8	TGR	—
9	QGR	—
10	WAGR	—
11-15	QGR	—
16	,,	Emu Bay No 16 (1948)
17	,,	Emu Bay No 18 (1953)
18-19	,,	—
20	WAGR	—
21-2	QGR	—
23	,,	Emu Bay No 17 (1948)
24-5	,,	—
26	WAGR	SAR No 305 (1951)
27-8	,,	—
29-32	,,	SAR Nos 302, 304, 301, 300 (1951)
33		Aus. Portland Cement No 3 (1945)
37-8	TGR	—
44-48	WAGR	—
49	,,	SAR No 303 (1951)
50	,,	—
51-53	QGR	—
54-59	WAGR	—
60-62	TGR	—
63-65	WAGR	—

For additional details of these locomotives,
refer to Chapter 5

WAR ENGINES

Class	Type	Cylinders Dia × Stroke (in)	Coupled Wheel Dia (ft in)	Boiler Press (psi)	Tractive Effort @ 75% (lb)	Grate Area (sq ft)	Max Boiler Dia (Outs) (ft in)	Heating Surface Fire-box	sq ft Tubes	Super-heater	Weights in Working Order (Tons) Max Axle	Ad-hesive	Total	Water Cpcty (Gal)	Fuel Cpcty (Tons /Gal)	Literature Reference
WD Heavy Type																
	2-8-2 + 2-8-2	19×24	3-9½	180	51410	51·3	7-0	212·0	2328	470	13·13	103·7	151·8	4600	9t	L98/43
	4-8-2 + 2-8-4	19×24	3-9½	180	51410	51·3	7-0	212·0	2328	470	13·25	105·85	171·5	6000	12t	
WD Light Type																
	2-8-0 + 0-8-2	15½×20	3-3	200	36960	43·7	5-7⅞	187	1555	313	10·5	83·75	103·35	2000	5t	
	2-8-2 + 2-8-2	15½×20	3-3	200	36960	43·7	5-8⅞	187	1555	313	10·5	83·45	117·85	3600	6t	
	4-8-2 + 2-8-4	16×24	4-0	200	38400	48·75	6-0	183	1813	399	10·0	80·0	136·8	4200	7t	
CLTB – Australian Standard Garratt																
ASG	4-8-2 + 2-8-4	14¼×24	4-0	200	30400	35	5-6	163	1535	315	8·5	68	119	4200	6t	G277/44 L145/43

Appendix

The Garratt and the Future

When the original edition of *The Garratt Locomotive* was published, in 1969, the world oil crisis had not developed, and it was comfortably assumed that the 2ft gauge SAR machines of 1968 were the World's last new Garratts. However, in the latter half of the 1970s, the severe oil shortage, leading to excessive escalation in oil prices, has led to diesel traction becoming increasingly uneconomic. Where sufficient traffic density exists, electrification is a solution, but on routes of lesser density, and where coal is available, the steam locomotive reappears as a very viable alternative. Zimbabwe, as has been seen in chapter 9, is rehabilitating Garratts for further service, reversing a previous policy of phasing out steam by 1980, while Zambia has resuscitated several Garratts previously disused. In several other parts of the world, steam traction is being actively retained or considered, and the resumption of steam locomotive production, probably in a more advanced or sophisticated form, is no longer out of the question, once current prejudice and inertia have been overcome.

The recent development of the fluidised bed boiler opens up new possibilities in the efficient use of even low quality coal, while the simpler gas producer system is in operation in Argentina, where it was developed by Ing.L.D.Porta, and in South Africa. Dr John Sharpe of Queen Mary College, London, has developed a mathematical model of a high efficiency steam locomotive, and it is most interesting to note that the Garratt format has been chosen as the most suitable vehicle for a modern, high power and high efficiency steam locomotive. The author has also entered this controversial field in a paper entitled 'Steam Locomotion — a reappraisal for an oil-starved World', read to the Institution of Mechanical Engineers in Bulawayo; and subsequently winning the C. N. Goodall award from the Institution in London. One of the illustrations in the author's paper was a high capacity Garratt to suit the South African axle load and loading gauge, and rather more than double the capacity of the GMAM, SAR's largest Garratt today.

At the time of writing there are not, so far as the author is aware, any firm proposals for building new Garratts, but the declining availability of the World's oil, with increasing dependence on coal, make new steam power, and new Garratts, an intriguing possibility!

Abbreviations

In both the text and tabular sections of this work abbreviations have been used in order to avoid repeating the longer titles used. These are listed below:

ABR	Assam Bengal Rly	ISR	Indian State Rlys
ASG	Australian Standard Garratt	KUR	Kenya Uganda Rly
BAP	Buenos Aires Pacific Rly	LMS	London Midland & Scottish Rly
BAR	Bengal Assam Rly	LNER	London & North Eastern Rly
BNR	Bengal Nagpur Rly	NBL	North British Locomotive Co
BP	Beyer Peacock & Co Ltd	NCCR	New Cape Central Rly
BR	British Railways	NER	North Eastern Rly
CA	Central of Aragon Rly	NEFR	North East Frontier Rly
CFB	Benguela Rly	NGR	Nepal Govt Rly
CFE	Ethiopian Rlys	NSW	New South Wales
CFL	Luanda Rly	NSWGR	New South Wales Govt Rlys
CFM	Moçambique Rlys	NZGR	New Zealand Govt Rlys
CME	Chief mechanical engineer	ORC	Ottoman Rly Co
CO	Congo-Ocean Rly	PLM	Paris Lyon & Mediterranean Rly
EAR	East African Rlys	QGR	Queensland Govt Rlys
FC	Ferro Carril	RC	Rotary cam poppet valves
FCAB	Antofagasta (Chile) and Bolivia Rly	RENFE	Spanish National Rlys
FCC	Central Rly of Peru	RR	Rhodesia Railways
FCER	Entre Rios Rly	SAR	South African Rlys
FCM	Midland Rly of Buenos Aires	SAR	South Australian Rlys (Chapter 5 only)
FCNER	Argentine North Eastern Rly	SNCV	Vicinal Rlys (Belgium)
Fr-B	Franco-Belge	SR	Sudan Rlys
GC	Great Central Rly	TGR	Tasmanian Govt Rlys
GCR	Gold Coast Rlys	TR	Tanganyika Rlys
HStP	Haine St Pièrre	TZR	Trans-Zambesi Rlys
		VFRGS	Rio Grande do Sul Rlys
		VGR	Victorian Govt Rlys
		WAGR	Western Australian Govt Rlys
		WD	War Dept

Bibliography

In the preparation of this book, the author has consulted the works listed below, all of which can be recommended for those wishing to study the subject further. Within the tables of principal dimensions included with each chapter will be found a column marked 'Literature reference', consisting of the initials of the reference work concerned, together with the page number and, if a periodical, the year of issue. These will enable researchers to look up the full technical descriptions of various Garratts as issued by the manufacturers when built.

(W)   *Articulated Locomotives* (Wiener)
(Q)   *Beyer Peacock Quarterly Review*
(H)   *Henschel Review*
        Institution of Locomotive Engineers Bulletins
        Articulated Locomotives (Kitson-Clark)
        Modern Articulated Locomotive (W. C. Williams)
        Steam on the RENFE (Marshall)
        Steam on the Sierra (Allen & Wheeler)
        Far Wheels (Small)
        Twenty-four Inches Apart (Moir)
(G)   *Railway Gazette*
(RE)   *Railway Engineer*
        Railway Engineering (SA)
        Railways of the Andes (Fawcett)
        Railways of Australia (Singleton & Burke)
(L)   *The Locomotive Railway Carriage & Wagon Review*
        Locomotive Panorama (Cox)
        South African Railways & Harbours Magazine
        Universal Directory of Railway Officials (Railway Year Book)

Abbott, R. *The Fairlie Locomotive.* David & Charles, 1970.

Allen, P. C. and Wheeler, R. A. *Steam on the Sierra.* Cleaver Hume, 1970.

Berridge, P. S. A. *Couplings to the Khyber.* David & Charles, 1969.

Butrims, R. *Australian Garratt.* Geelong Steam Preservation/ARHS 1975.

Colquhoun, Stewein & Thomas. *Proceed to Peterborough.* ARHS 1970.

Cox, E. S. *Locomotive Panorama, Vol 1.* Ian Allan 1965.

Cox, E. S. *Chronicles of Steam.* Ian Allan 1967.

Croxton, A. H. *Railways of Rhodesia.* David & Charles 1973.

Durrant, A. E. *The Garratt Locomotive.* David & Charles 1969.

Durrant, A. E. *The Mallet Locomotive.* David & Charles 1974.

Durrant, A. E. *Australian Steam.* David & Charles 1978.

Durrant, A. E., Jorgensen, A. A., & Lewis C. P. *Steam on the Veld.* Ian Allan 1972.

Durrant, A. E., Jorgensen, A. A., & Lewis C. P. *Steam in Africa.* Struik 1981.

Fawcett, B. *Railways of the Andes.* Allen & Unwin 1965.

Fawcett, B. *Steam in the Andes.* Bradford Barton 1973.

Gunzburg, A. *WAGR Locomotives 1940–68.* ARHS 1968.

Holland, D. F. *Steam Locomotives of the South African Railways* (2 vols). David & Charles 1971.

Hughes, H. C. *Steam in India.* Bradford Barton 1976.

Hughes, H. C. *Steam Locomotives in India (Vol 2, metre gauge)* Continental Railway Circle, 1977.

Hughes, H. C. *Steam Locomotives in India (Vol 3, broad gauge)* Continental Railway Circle, 1979.

Jorgensen, A. A., & Lewis, C. P. *The Great Steam Trek.* Struik 1978.

Marshall, B., & Wilson J. *Locomotives of the SAR.* ARHS 1972.

Marshall, L. G. *Steam on the RENFE.* Macmillan, 1965.

McClaire, E. J. *The NZR Garratt Story.* NZRLS 1978.

Moir, S. M. *Twenty Four Inches Apart.* Oakwood Press, 1963.

Obregon, A. M. *Memorias del Ferrocarril del Sur.* (Ecuador) 1977.

Palmer, A. N., & Stewart, W. W. *Cavalcade of NZR Locomotives.* Angus & Robertson, 1965.

Preston, R. G. *NSWGR in Steam.* ARHS 1978.

Purdom, D. S. *British Steam on the Pampas.* Mechanical Engineering Publications, 1977.

Ramear, R. *Steam Locomotives of East Africa.* David & Charles 1974.

Small, C. S. *Far Wheels.* Cleaver Hume.

Talbot, E. *Steam from Kenya to the Cape.* Continental Railway Circle 1975.

Weiner, L. *Articulated Locomotives.* Constable, 1930.

A Century Plus of Locomotives. (NSW). ARHS 1965.

Locomotives of the LNER, part 9B. RCTS 1977.

G42 — Puffing Billy's Big Brother. Puffing Billy Society 1981.

Rhodesia Railways Museum. Rhodesia Railways, 1975.

Steam in South Africa and Rhodesia. World Steam, 1976.

Periodicals

Beyer Peacock Quarterly Review
Henschel Review
The Locomotive
The Railway Gazette
Continental Railway Journal
World Steam
ARHS Bulletins
The Narrow Gauge
Proceedings of the Institution of Locomotive Engineers

House magazines; East African Railways, Rhodesia
Railways, South African Railways.

Locomotive builders' catalogues

Beyer Garratt (circa 1908, 1925, 1930 and 1947)
Ansaldo
Armstrong Whitworth
Haine St. Pierre
Henschel
Krauss-Maffei
Krupp
St. Leonard

Official diagram books

F.C. de La Robla
RENFE
RSR Thailand

Bas Congo Katanga
C.F. Benguela
C.F. Moçambique
East Africa
Rhodesia
South Africa
NSWGR
South Australia
Queensland
WAGR
F.C. Belgrano
B.A.G.S.R.
F.C. Entre Rios

Report

Of the Royal Commission on the Australian Standard
Garratt. Government Printer, Perth, 1946.

Acknowledgements

In the preparation of both this book, and the preceding tome 'The Garratt Locomotive', the author has received much assistance from various railways, locomotive builders, and enthusiasts all over the world, as listed below. The greatly extended bibliography reveals the extent to which worldwide interest in the steam locomotive has increased over the past decade, with many books now published which would previously have been unviable. That so many of these books include Garratt information is most gratifying.

Railways which have helped by providing information, photographs, or assistance with the author's travels, either by post or frequently by friendly officials, have been:

Antofogasta (Chile) and Bolivia Railway
Angola Railways
Benguela Railway
Belgrano Railway
British Railways
Catalan Railways
F.C. Iquique a Pueplo Hundido
East African Railways
Ghana Railways
Indian Railways
Malawi Railways
Moçambique Railways
Moçamedes Railway
New South Wales Railways
New Zealand Railways
Nigerian Railways
Queensland Railways
Rhodesia Railways/National Railways of Zimbabwe
South African Railways
South Australian Railways
Santos — Jundiai Railway
S.N.C. Vicinaux
Sudan Railways
Tasmanian Government Railways
Royal State Railways of Thailand
Victorian Railways
Western Australian Government Railways.

Builders and other organisations who have been helpful are:

Beyer Peacock
Babcock & Wilcox (Bilbao)
Crown Agents
English Electric
Euskalduna
Franco Belge
General Steel Castings, Inc.
Krauss Maffei
Krupp
RESCCO, Bulawayo
SKF (South Africa)
British Timken.

Of the numerous enthusiasts who have helped, most of whose names appear in the photographic credits, especial mention must be made of Messrs G. S. Moore, who supplied much of the detail on builders' numbers and dates, and H. C. Hughes for his valuable detail on Indian Garratts. D. R. Carling wrote several long letters full of useful notes, following publication of the original Garratt book. Alan Wild, of the Bournemouth Railway Club, took great pains to obtain good prints from the Kelland negatives. Most important of all, thanks to my wife Christine for assistance in the darkroom, companionship chasing Garratts and patience when I am absent, or incarcerated in my study! Christine must be one of very few ladies who have seen Garratts at work on four continents, and whose first footplate ride was on a Garratt!

Index